FRIENDS OF ALICE PUBLISHING

LOVE ON THE ISLE OF DOGS

JUDE COWAN MONTAGUE is an artist, poet, musician. Born in Manchester, she has lived mostly in London. At the age of 21 she went to Sumatra and learned to sing saluang songs and has been an alternative musician all her adult life. She worked as an archivist for Reuters Television Archive for ten years and has written poetry and made art about international news stories. She is a broadcaster and runs the weekly show The News Agents for Resonance FM. She plays Hammond Organ and has a husky.

LOVE ON THE ISLE OF DOGS is a graphic memoir of her life in the 1990s. It is a story about everyday challenge of becoming a young parent, getting married and living independently in a London that seems to have already vanished in the 2020s. It is a story of severe mental health, awareness of psychosis, living with these problems and surviving in her own way. Most of all, this is a personal love story. In which, as we all know, anything can happen.

Also by Jude Cowan Montague

FOR THE MESSENGERS (Donut Press, 2011)

THE GROODOYALS OF TERRE ROUGE (Dark Windows Press, 2013)

THE WIRES: 2012 (WB Press, 2016)

THE ORIGINALS (Hesterglock Press, 2017)

Printed and bound by imprintdigital.com, Upton Pyne, Exeter

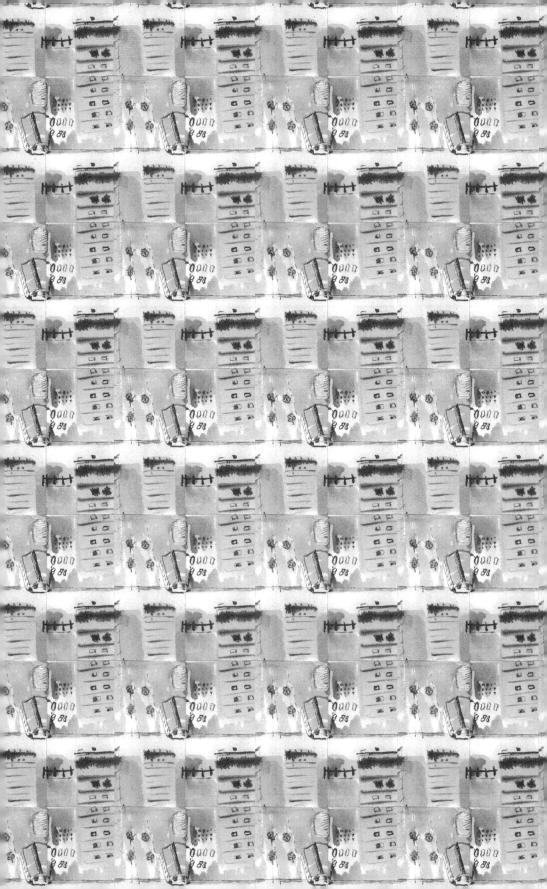

LOVE ON THE ISLE OF DOGS

FRIENDS OF ALICE
- PUBLISHING-

978-1-9160306-7-1

JUDE COWAN MONTAGUE

LOVE ON THE ISLE OF DOGS

FRIENDS OF ALICE PUBLISHING 2020

ACKNOWLEDGEMENTS

Thanks go to my editor Isabel del Rio, Matt Armstrong, my daughter Blanaid Montague, my mum and dad, Charles Easmon, Sanjeev Bhaskar and my friends from the Tom Allen Arts Centre, Emily Haworth-Booth, my classmates from evening class at the Royal Drawing School and the organisers and members of Laydeez do Comics.

DEDICATION

To all those in trouble

CONTENTS

INTRODUCTION

This story has three protagonists: a woman, a man, and their home. Each is enchanting and strange. The woman is resourceful and practical, the hard-working manager of a community arts hub in east London. But she is also a closet romantic, drawn to impossible things. When she is young, she dreams about catching a star. As a grown-up, one falls into her lap: an 'old flame' who has single-handedly built his own house but, following a head injury, can't recall the word screwdriver. He too is brilliant, distant, and – yes – impossible.

They make their home in the Isle of Dogs, on the edge of a changing city. The only dockers in Docklands are now ghosts. The couple tries, instinctively, to strike a new deal with the landscape. During the first and happiest days of their marriage, he lays the stones for their garden while she plants the beds. At one point, he gives her some lilacs. 'I put them on the television in a glass jug,' she recalls. This lovely miscellany – television, glass, water, flower – reminds us of the diverse forms we pack, like resourceful gardeners, into our small living spaces. Inspired by his youthful show-jumping, she takes up horse-riding at a city farm. There is just a second of perfect balance when it seems like new life, and not just new money can flourish in London.

But this balance is untenable. Inside her husband, there is another world, full of puzzlement and suffering he can't explain. And worlds, in this tale, are contagious. We can't ignore where other people live. Little by little, our protagonist's experience of her surroundings grows distorted. Bridges become sinister lookouts, place-names a paranoid acrostic. London's notorious suddenness – turn a corner and you're in another world – feels like a metaphor for the way we live together, even and especially at home. Home itself becomes a battleground, a state of permanent emergency. Go Home Go Home Go Home! clamour well-meaning friends, which just overwhelms her. 'Are you trying to poison me?' asks her husband, no longer at home anywhere. And the black honeycomb of the hospital – the Royal London, here drawn with the density of nightmare – is an embodiment of the mad, implacable care system.

For all this drama about marriage, the book ends not with husband and wife, but with mother and child. From her first appearance, the protagonist's baby opens up her world. Movingly, she is in love with the child's new, bare feet: 'tentacles of a deep-sea creature.' She is no longer chasing after stars. This marine visitor shows her something deeper even than the landscape – though she gives that back to her, too. Sheep! the mother gasps, like an excited infant, taking her child to the city farm. Their relationship seems to offer a solution to the problem of others' needs which has, quite literally, dogged her. Even the couple's canine pet – a joyful free spirit – is destructive when left alone.

Montague's pictures are the stars of the book. They are wild, sudden and changeable. Sometimes they almost look like weather fronts, keeping pace with unpredictable moods and events. A motif that on one page glows with humour, and on the next turns threatening and dark. Pools of ink resemble tears or water. Some lines are spindly, almost hasty, reminding us of the hand that drew them, perhaps in desperation. This style allows Montague to mix the comic and the devastating. She can move quickly when she needs to and then linger on what she can't forget. It also helps her in her other project: representing the 90s, when her tale takes place. Montague cites the German expressionist Ernst Kirchner as a key influence – especially his pictures of mountains, whose bright, wavy lines make them feel almost domestic. Here, it is society which is cut down to size. Map-like pictograms reveal the huge structures of government – the attainment of targets and the rationing of funds – with people's lives bulldozed at the crossroads. We also see a city changing, new buildings, and new commercial industries rising on pile-driven foundations, skyscrapers reminiscent of the old New York.

Love on the Isle of Dogs emerges at a moment when the UK is once again in various kinds of flux. Wherever we stand on the nation's future, this extraordinary book reminds us we all stand on the same landscape, making what we can of our shared lives. As a memoir, it has a clean, clear narrative – an encounter with chaos and darkness, which ends with a return to something like normality. But its pictures push beyond this personal story. Each page gives vivid form to movement until it feels like the biographer's real subject – a dog playing, a city changing, cars in a tunnel, someone going mad.

Ben Morgan, poet
Medea in Corinth (Poetry Salzburg)

LOVE ON THE ISLE OF DOGS

Part One

Pictures

Love Love Love Love Love Love Love Love Love Love Love Love Love Love Love Love Love Love Love Love

it's a True Story

when I was a child
the nights were dark

I saw a star

It fell into my hand

23

25

I BOUGHT
ALL MY CLOTHES
FROM CHARITY SHOPS

OXFAM

BOXES OF DRESSES
FOR
50p

OR FROM
BRICK
LANE

GENTS
SHOES

THE JEWISH
MARKETS

into the Blackwall Tunnel

We slept surrounded by the sounds
of construction, buildings going up
all around.

our stars shining down

He played
music that reminded him of home

My dad had loved Percy French

He laughed as he told me this story about a policeman "defusing" a suspect burger box.

He laughed a LOT really a LOT

He had been
a
Champion
show jumper
at
school

I wanted to go riding too

(and I did, inspired by him, at the local city farm)

I knew this story
from before ...

... one night,
cycling home,
he had seen...

bright
lights

40

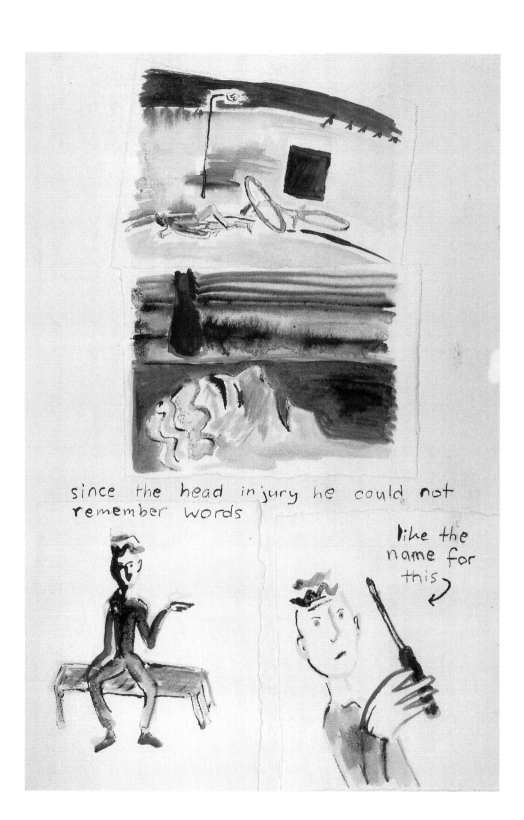

since the head injury he could not remember words

like the name for this ⟶

Sometimes,
he would quietly
look at
NOTHING

especially
in the
evening

is
everythin
ok?

at night
things could
turn

he could turn
what was he
worried about?

43

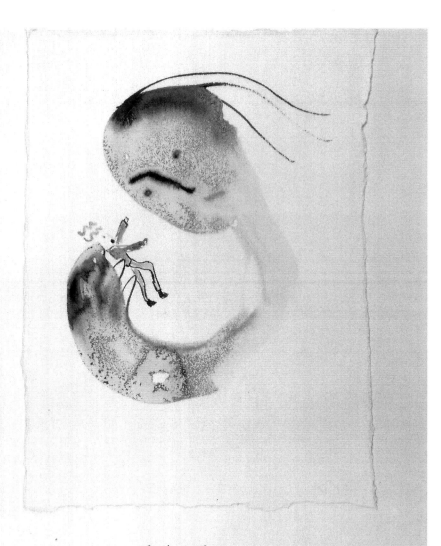

could I
help him?

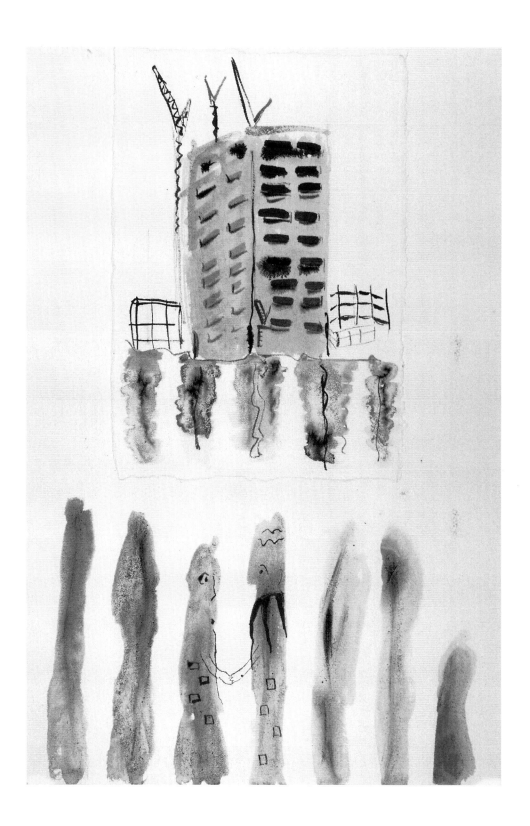

45

LOVE on the Isle of Dogs

PART TWO
Marriage

11. 04. 1992

49

where
are
we
going?

Everything
will be
okay

You're not
on your own
any more

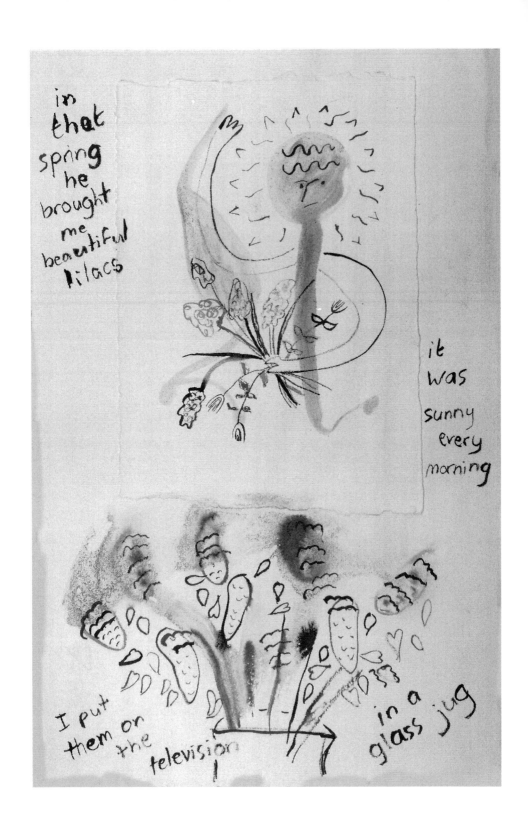

in that spring he brought me beautiful lilacs

it was sunny every morning

I put them on the television

in a glass jug

<u>the garden</u>

he laid the stones by hand

I planted
the
beds

Time to explore

What was this strange land, THE ISLE OF DOGS?

a land of workers

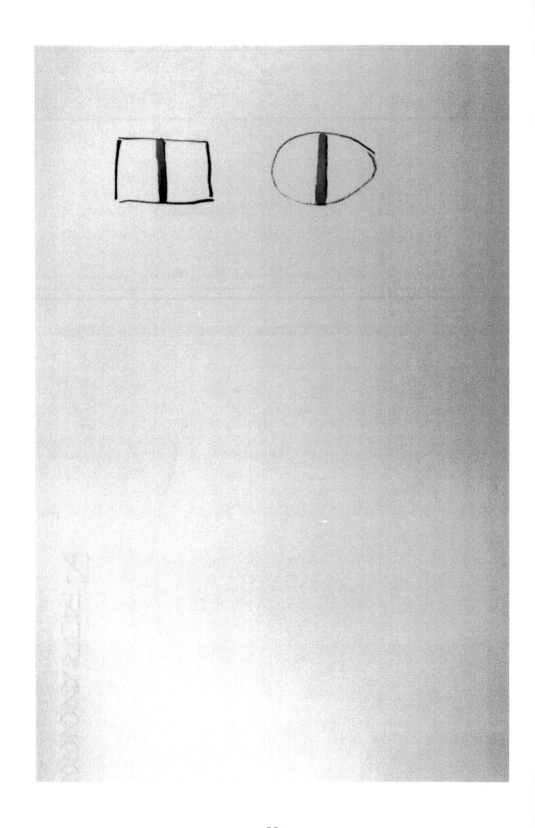

PART THREE
PREGNANCY

ROYAL LONDON HOSPITAL

spinning, flicking,
dancing, never still

OUR BABY

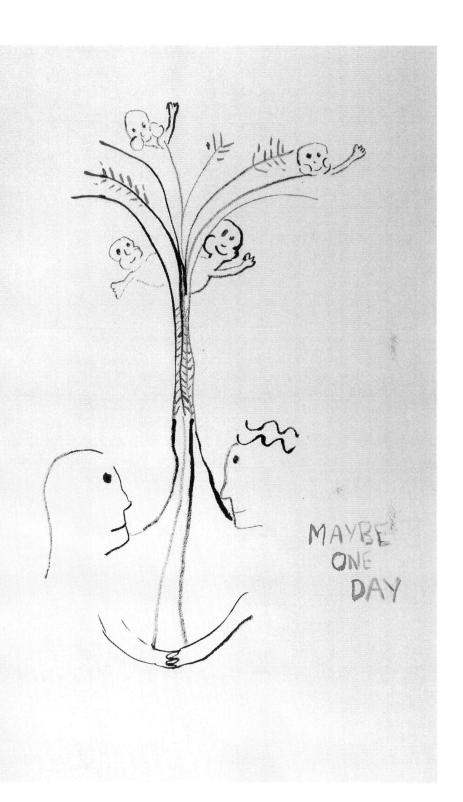

MAYBE
ONE
DAY

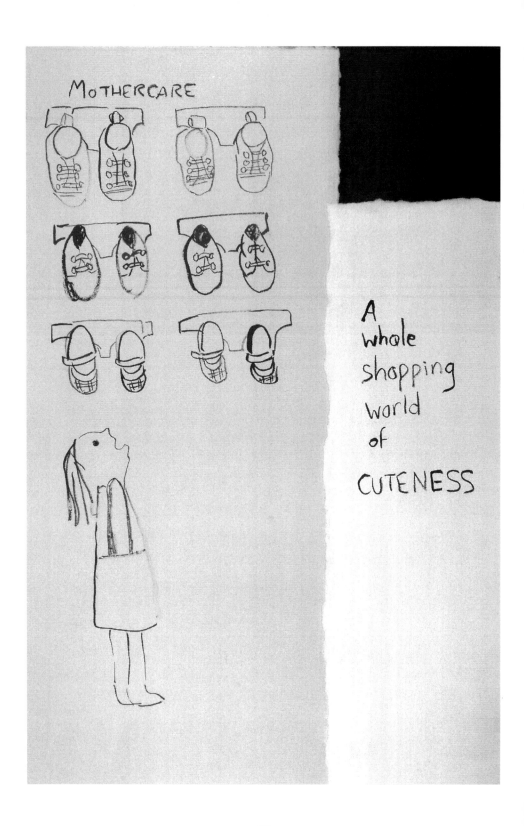

MOTHERCARE

A whole shopping world of CUTENESS

ORDER BECAME IMPORTANT

WHICH STONE IN WHICH ORDER?

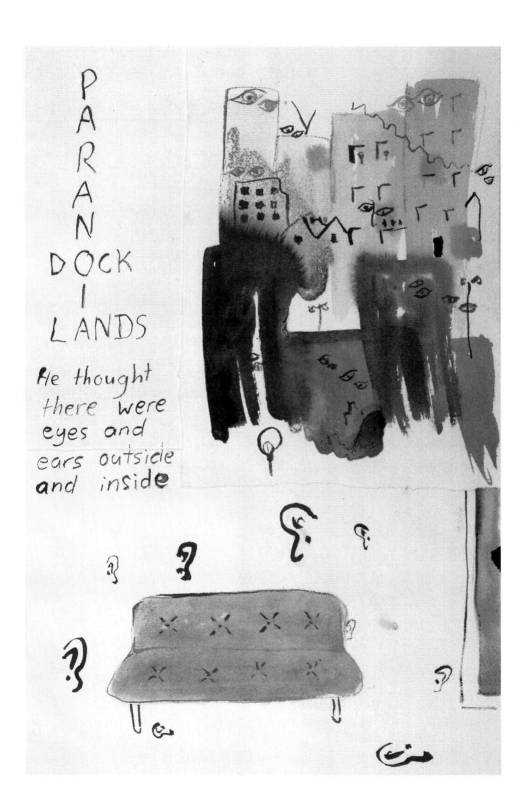

PARANOI
DOCK
LANDS

He thought
there were
eyes and
ears outside
and inside

I tried
to
entertain
him

it felt like I was
running
in
circles

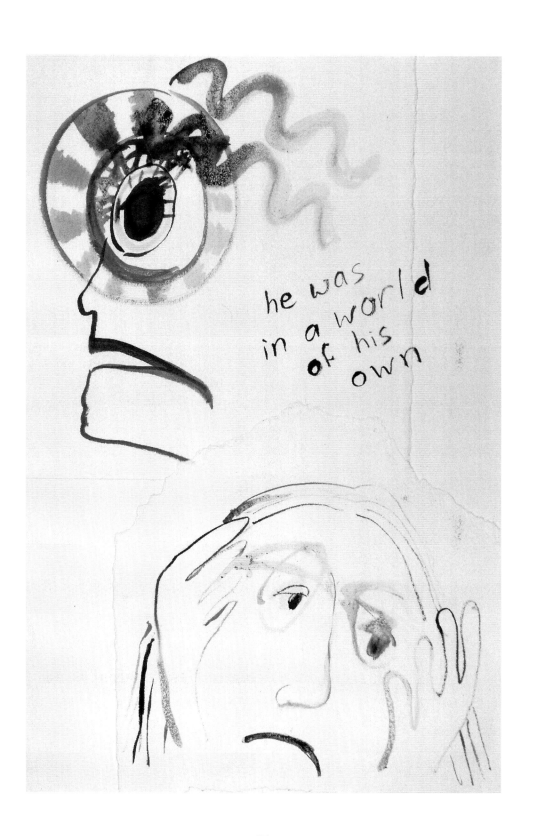

he was
in a world
of his
own

I felt
shadows
watching
me

from the lookouts
on the
many bridges

the fences
closed
us in

THEN someone else wonderful came into my life

thanks to him

PART FOUR
BIRTH AND...

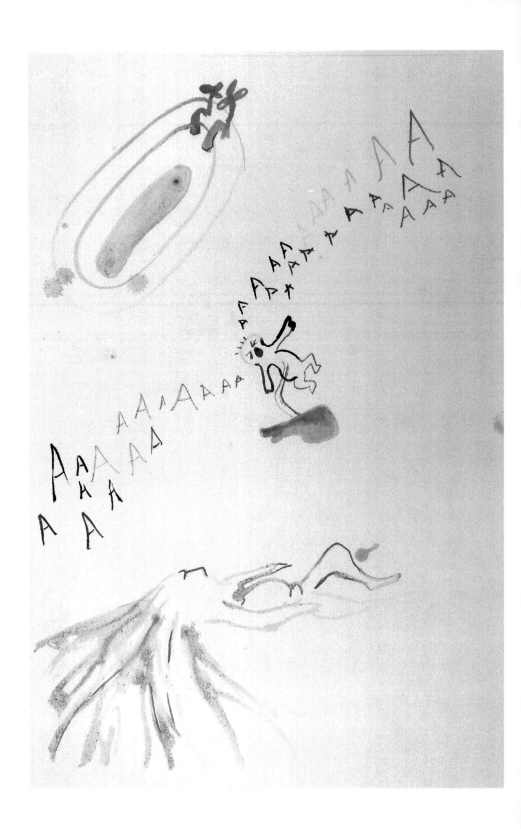

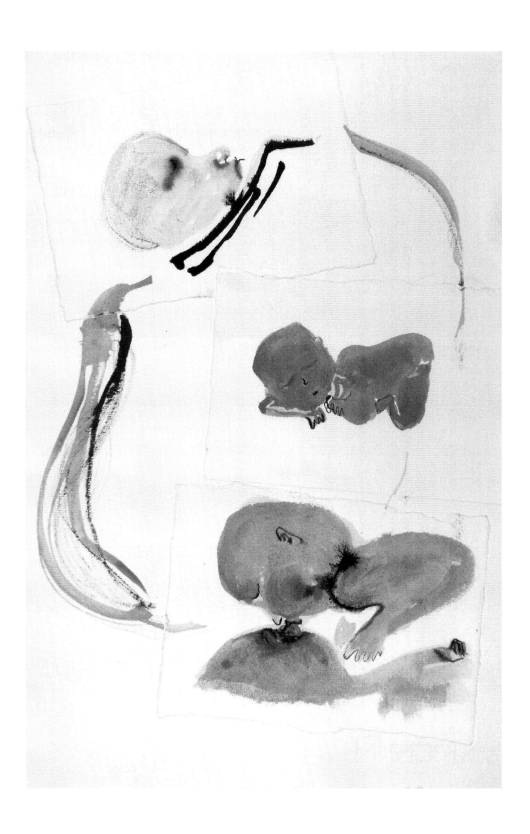

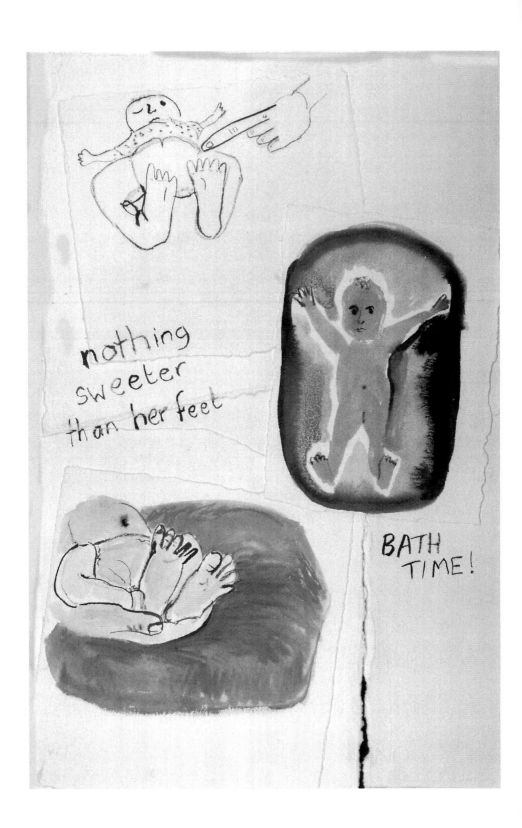

nothing
sweeter
than her feet

BATH
TIME!

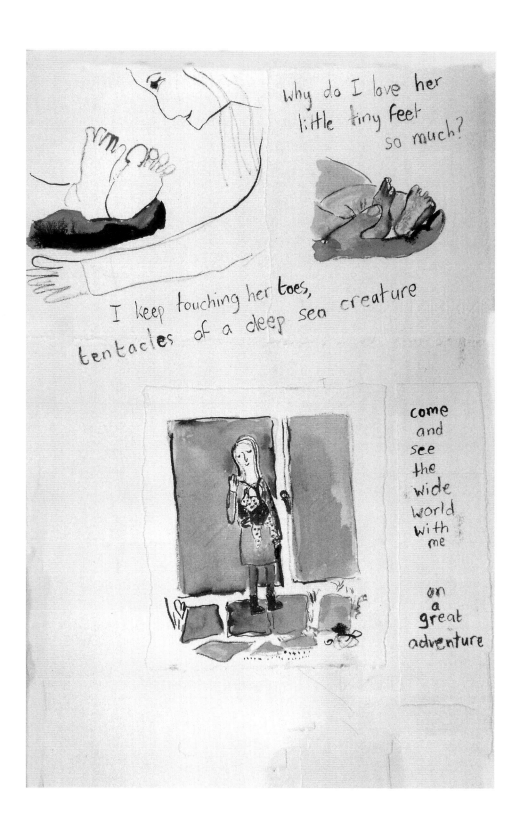

why do I love her little tiny feet so much?

I keep touching her toes, tentacles of a deep sea creature

come
and
see
the
wide
world
with
me

on
a
great
adventure

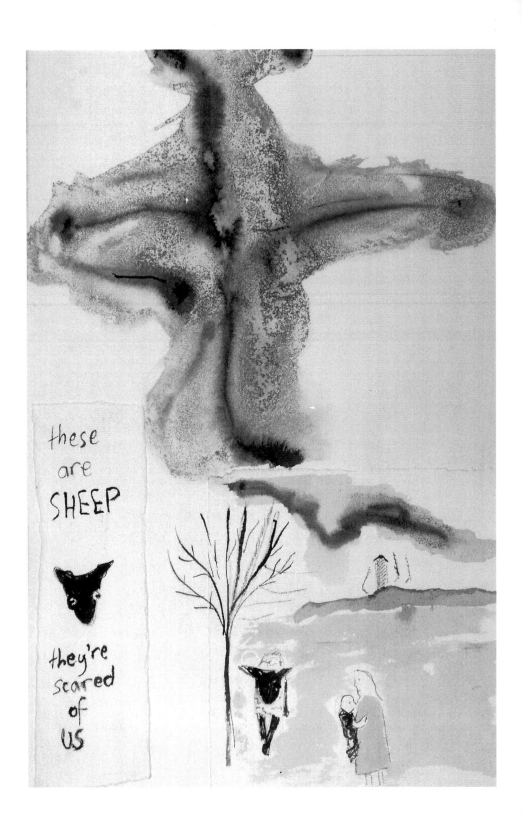

these
are
SHEEP

they're
scared
of
US

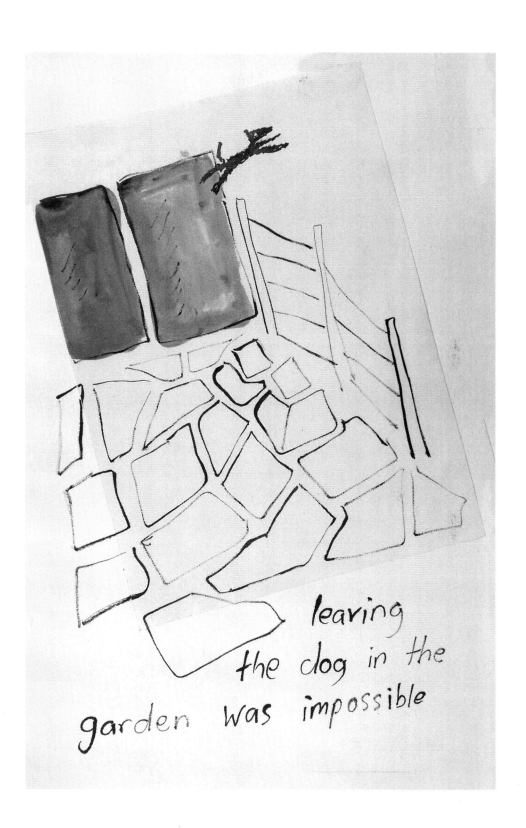

leaving
the dog in the
garden was impossible

is this your dog?

The dog catcher
threatened to take him
away —
he might be
put down!

When we went shopping We could
hear her bark and bark
So we thought she might
be happier in the car

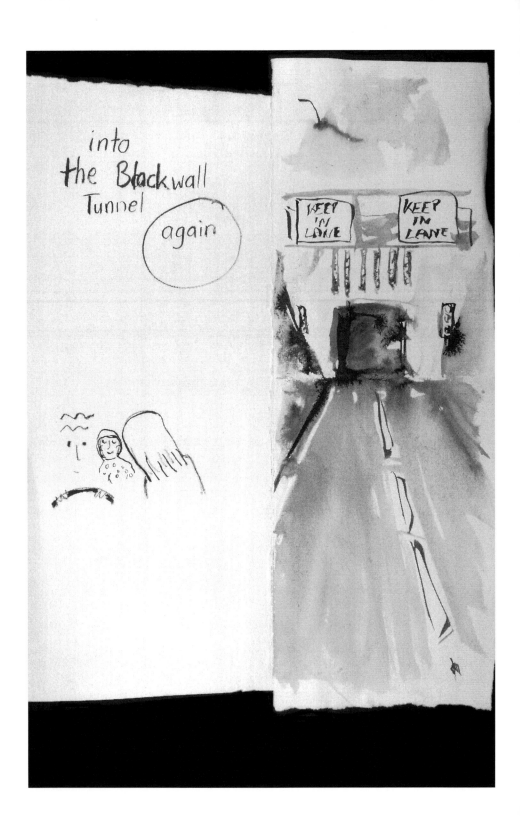

I couldn't understand
what was happening

He didn't seem to know
who he was

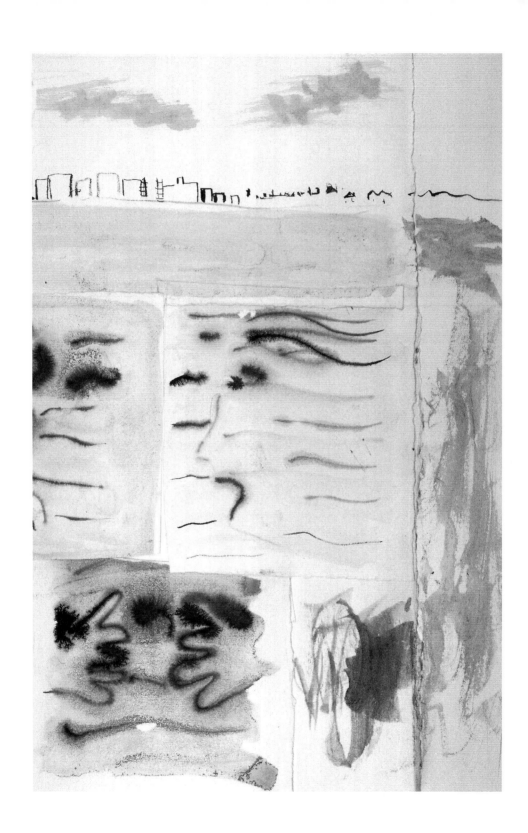

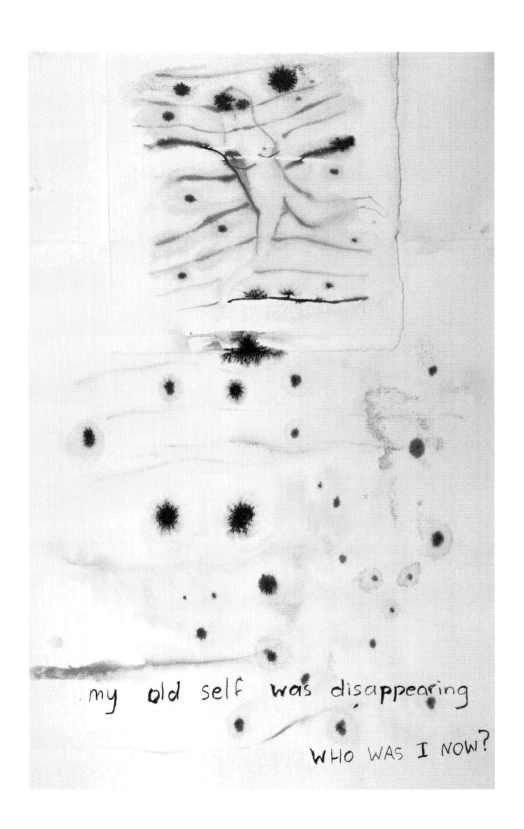

my old self was disappearing

WHO WAS I NOW?

He thought people were lying to him including his mother

Dear John,
I think you may be my father...

He wrote strange letters to his uncle

HIS BEST FRIEND SAID

"it's the trauma of the birth"

TRUST HIM

becoming a father

"we have to believe him"

99

Part Five

MADNESS AND PILLS

THE ROYAL LONDON HOSPITAL

He disappeared inside

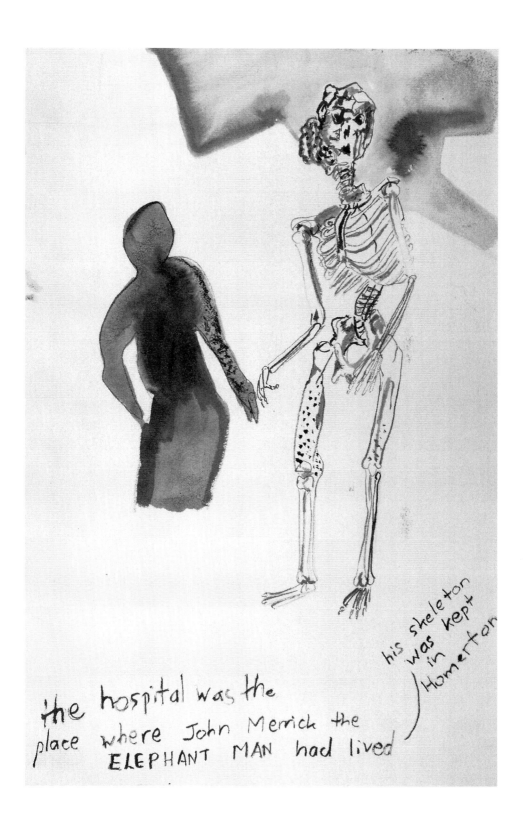

his skeleton was kept in Homerton

the hospital was the place where John Merrick the ELEPHANT MAN had lived

the covered face,
the Victorian streets

I'd seen
the David
Lynch film
at the
cinema

one night
in
OLD LONDON

"the blue flashes...
the jolting...
the noise"
SYLVIA
PLATH

MENTAL HEALTH TREATMENT
in books
sounded like torture

We didn't see the doctor much. When
we went in together she was kind to us both.

109

6 AM

9 AM

11 AM

12 NOON

2 PM

4 PM

6 PM

8 PM

10 PM

In the tradition of modern artists he took
photographs of the street outside at different
times of day
and from different angles

they all looked the same,
washed out, lifeless, colourless

So when the nurse asked me privately . . .

"are you sure you're okay if he comes home?"
I said
"oh yes"

Regional Secure Unit

Powell's Water Tower

General Hospital

Psychiatric Unit

COMMUNITY CARE

MENTAL HOSPITAL

shutting down

HOME

HOSPITAL

LOCAL AUTHORITY

£?

Where do you go? Where could we go?

The COMMUNITY

family doctor

Patient's family home

Short Stay Hostel

Long Stay Accommodation

We were are the community

We were in the middle of

A National Debate on Mental Health SERVICES

Funding

117

WHO ARE YOU?

PART SIX

121

The drugs
slowed down his speech

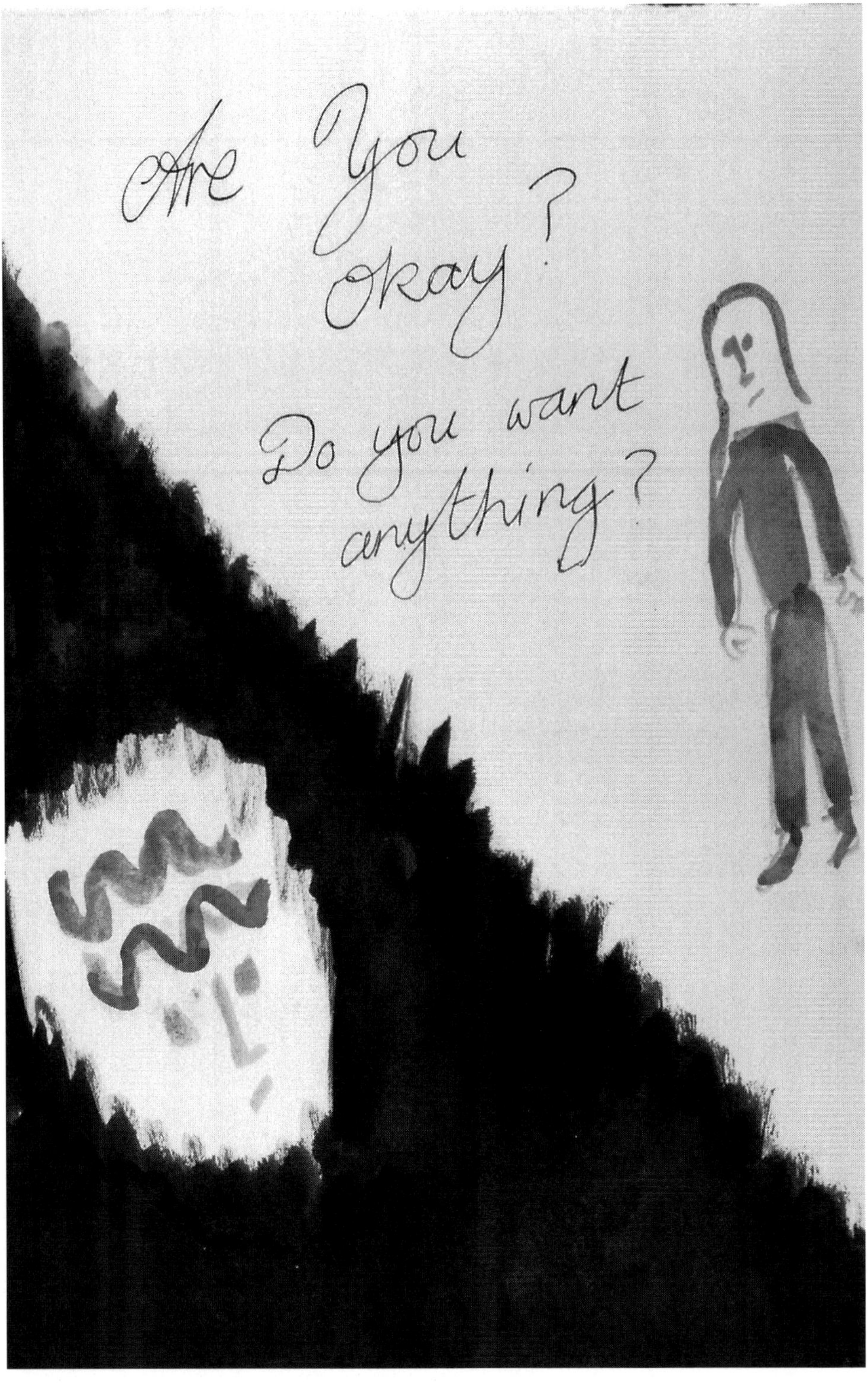
Are You
Okay?
Do you want
anything?

INTO THE

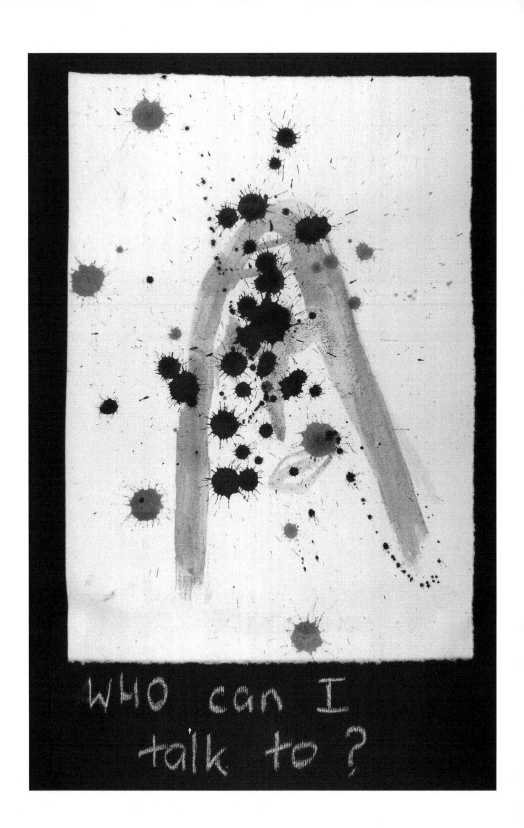

WHO can I
talk to ?

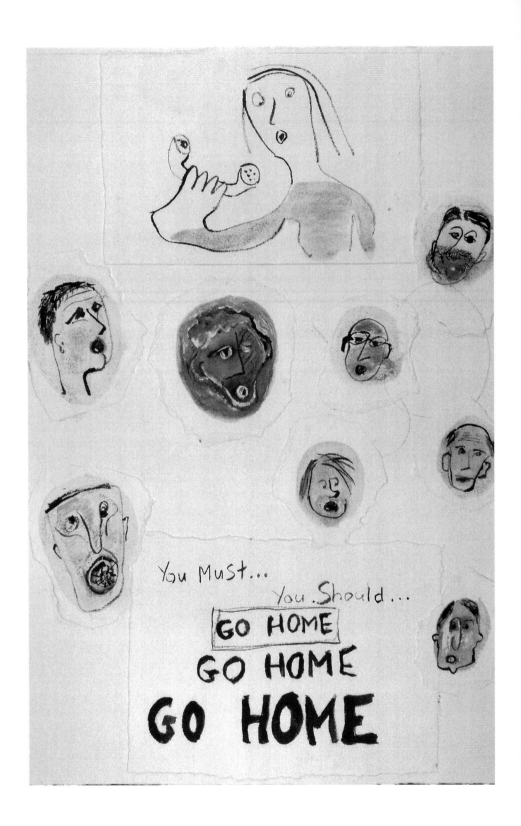

time out!

playing table
tennis with
Sanjeev from
work

(now he's really famous
for Goodness Gracious Me etc)

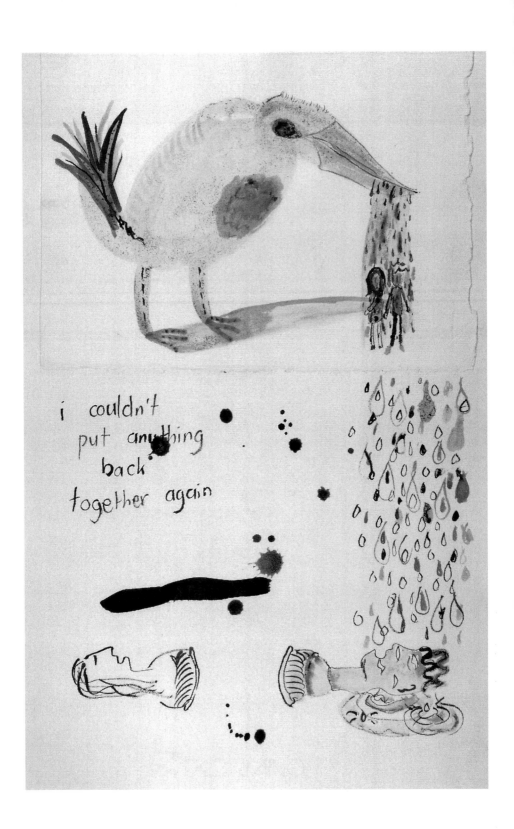

i couldn't
put anything
back
together again

133

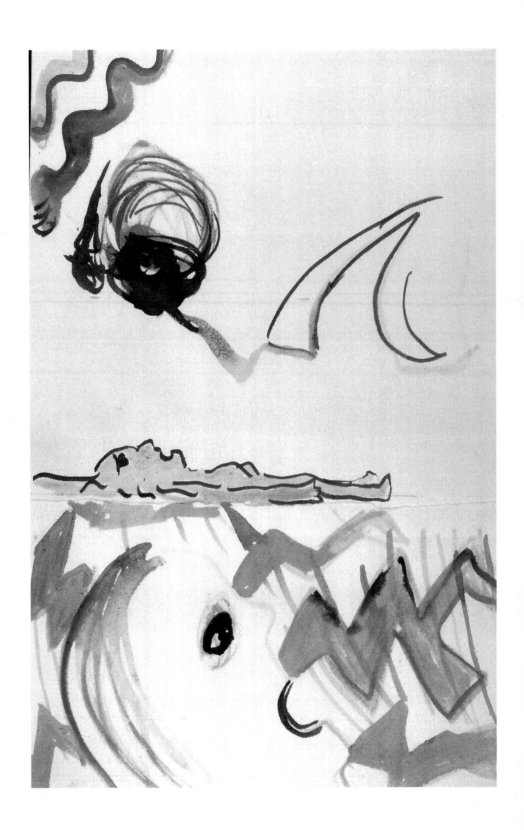

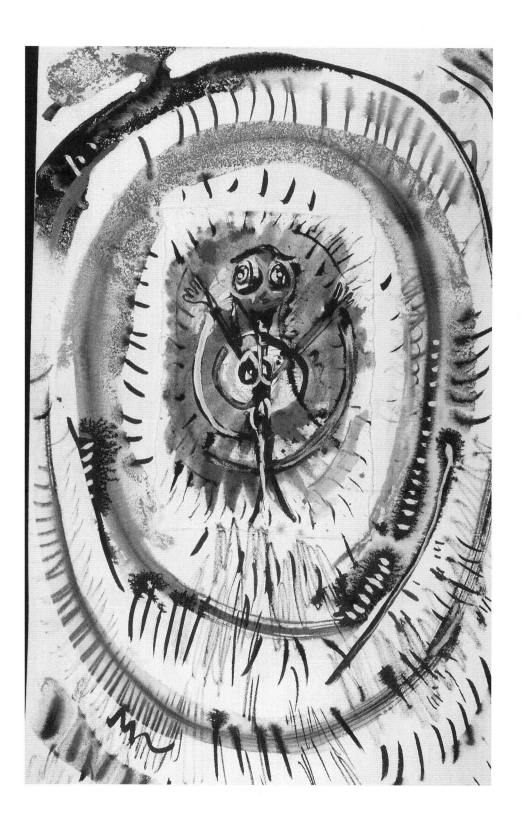

LOVE ON THE ISLE OF DOGS

Part Two

Words

There were many more stars when I was young. But I was always looking for my own star out there. I'd give it a name when I found it. But I could never make up my mind which star was mine. I looked though the gaps between the brighter, obvious stars for a special one that no one had ever found before. I wanted a star that had defeated science, eluded Jodrell Bank's super-scopes.

Of course, what can a child ever hope to discover that the scientists had missed? There were no secrets left for me to be the first to stumble on. Lessons were all about learning what other people had done before, then trying to do those things as well as I could. My role was to walk the line that the adults drew for me. This wasn't painful, not too painful. There were lots of words to learn. Diagrams to draw. Exercises to complete. I liked exercises. I enjoyed exams.

I know this is a bit holier-than-thou.

I enjoyed exams.

I know that sounds...

... like you should shut this book right now. Dislike me just as much as the girls at school did, for being a swot.

But I was never the kind of swot who did what they were told. I did go on an adventure. But it wasn't like our head girl who set out to swim the English Channel, covered in blubber, stroke after stroke after stroke, keeping up with the boat in the grey waves of freezing La Manche.

When I found a star, it fell into my hand.

But it burnt me, so I let it go.

One day, I was minding my own business. Or rather I was minding everyone else's business. Because at that time of my life I was a publicity officer. I worked for a crazy little arts centre, nestled, out of sight, down a little cul-de-sac in the housing blocks of Newham. A former boxing club, the ring was now a theatre space. It would be repurposed for different shows. Come on, move those rostrums. And front of house would reluctantly get into gear. But I didn't have to shift my arse into gear. Because I was a publicity officer. I got to do other stuff. Like design posters and talk to the press, and do admin. I had to keep the turnover high. Be seen to be busy.

Surrounded by boxes of leaflets, I can see myself now, in jeans, jumper, scruffy straw hair, pale and interesting, getting ready for the great mailout. But I can't focus on my face for long, I shift to the equipment around me, the things that were different about life in the 1990s from life in 2020. It's quite bizarre to me today to think how much we spent on posting those leaflets out to the families of Newham. What did they think when that glossy leaflet, designed by me, (yes, me, what a thrill, what a worry, how terrifying!) arrived on their carpets, plop through the letterbox. And we didn't even have to go to the post office. We had a franking machine. It stamped pale red prices in the top right-hand corner of the envelope with a satisfying clunk. Yummy.

I put on the radio and began to stuff. And stuff. I enjoyed it.

Repeat to the beat. Reggae and roll.

La la la. The radio is playing now, I can hear it, fizzing, the inane chat of the DJs, the crackle of the charts. Sounds are better through an FM filter. Back then, music was life. Filling envelopes was rhythm.

Sometimes I thought I should have worked in a factory. I'd have loved the routine of the repetition so long as I could listen to music.

I can't remember what I was listening to when my heart stopped.

The door was always open. This was an arts centre. It was a drop-in centre, really. People were always hanging around telling us their problems, confiding in us. It was less institutional, less needy than hanging out with social workers. They'd come to the drama workshops and never go home.

But the door being open made us vulnerable to the outside world. With the door kept open, anything could blow in off the street at any time. And anyone could come in. Including Him.

'Hello,' he said. Casually. Darkly. Cheerfully.

'Oh. Yeah, hello.'

Thump. Thump. Blood in my ears. Blood in my face. Looking at the floor, I said, 'What brings you to this neck of the woods.'

'Looking for you.'

The way he said the word 'you' trapped me. He knew how to say words. He knew how to put the right emphasis on them. He knew how to make them important. When he said, 'Looking for you' it made me important.

I wasn't that important. I was just a girl stuffing envelopes, singing along to the radio. Okay, I was a lucky girl, I got to design the leaflets that

150

I stuffed.

I was sitting in a pool of bright light. He was a shadow.

I could barely look in his eyes. Dark like the unseen parts of the carpet, like the under-seat of a chair, like the secret nothing beneath the desk or at the back of the drawers. Like the inside of the computer whose green writing was spies and stars, whispers from a paranoid movie. I couldn't look at him. I sat in the dark.

I thought about nothing. I thought about music. I couldn't remember the names of any bands. A guitar riff from a Ghanaian band rang around and around in my head, as if a guitar was riding a carousel. It went from one ear to the other and back again.

I've never been one to hear voices but music – music that isn't there – I hear that all the time.

'I'm working,' I said.

'Okay, well, when do you finish?'

I told him.

We went for a drink.

I thought I'd never be able to swallow. My throat was hot and wide and there was no room for food or drink to go down. There was hardly any room for words.

I breathed slowly. It was hard at first to force the breaths to behave themselves, make them as steady as possible. But it got easier. I watched the woman cleaning the glasses on the bar. Easy-does-it. Clean the wine glass. Put it tail up on the shelf above the bar.

'I've built a house,' he said. 'Three stories. I've been doing a self-build. It's complete now. I've split up with D—. I'm ready to go out with you.'

Well, that was a turn-up. What about last time?

Last time I had ditched him as I felt he wasn't psychologically ready for a relationship with me. We'd got together, stars had collided. It had been a rollercoaster. A brief, almost-affair that never was. But he was too vulnerable.

Why?

Because.

He'd had.

An accident.

It had happened one night on the Isle of Dogs. After a day's work on the building site with his brother-in-law, he'd been cycling home, dusty and bothered. But was it the building site? Or was it once he'd gone back to college to learn his trade, furniture making at the London College of Furniture?

I wasn't there. How could I know? He was going out with his dark-haired girlfriend at the time. His childhood sweetheart, D—. They'd been at school together in Omagh. Petite, cute face, brown eyes, sensible. They'd be together forever. All the good ones are taken. My mum used to say, why are they single? Ask that. When men were older, if they were single there was a reason. Older probably meant over 25. I discarded my mother's advice. What did she know?

But maybe it was a good sign that he was in a long-term relationship, not that I was looking to break anything up. Oh no, I didn't see myself as a marriage wrecker. My friend's sister wore a badge on her greatcoat that said 'marriage wrecker'. That was wrong. But then I felt that chemistry. When the world is cooking with gas, the lids are going to blow. There'll be broken glass all over the laboratory.

He was cycling home and POW! Out of nowhere. Two lights, two bright lights bearing down on him.

He remembered nothing. Much. They found him. Someone found him on the road, called the ambulance. Whatever.

He saw a cracked ceiling. Heard the beep of the machine. The tiny aliens trying to talk to him. The room wouldn't come into focus. Spinning. Voices in and out. High and low pitched mutterings rising and falling like a million soufflés going in and out of the oven. Some English. Some international voices of the nurses and the doctors. What did those voices say about where he was? He couldn't tell. It wasn't Irish. Where were the Irish nurses? Where was he? This wasn't Tyrone. The traffic was too loud, too insistent, too roaring, too filthy, too ...

You're in the London Hospital, he was told. I have to get home, he said, trying to get out of bed.

Oh no you don't. You have to stay here. Who are you?

It turned out he couldn't even remember that. Or where he lived. Day by day, on hospital food, it came back to him. D— came to see him

152

after work. I suppose she was with him at the point his family came over from Tyrone to see him. Brothers and sisters, mostly sisters. Some lived in London already and went on errands for the rest of the family, allocated jobs, family jobs. A creaking machine, complaining but efficient. Older sister bossing the younger ones in the tribe. There was an uneasy truce between them all that allowed the work to be done effectively. They brought him grapes and music and books. And things to do. And the words came back, one after another.

When we had met for the first time, the words were returning in clumps. The regular, most commonly used words came back first. Then the rarer words. He held a tool in his hand.

'What is this?' he asked himself. 'What is this?' he asked me. It was a chisel. He answered himself.

The words were connecting up again. That bang on the head had juddered his knowledge out of line. They had to be put back one by one in everyday life. Meanwhile D— went to work and carried on climbing up the civil service ladder. S— and D— were different. And they gradually became more different.

I was the one more like him. Swimming in an indeterminate arty nebulous culture. Not working every day. Mixing with musicians and actors and odd misfits. Playing music and laughing at the world. Maybe not trying to change it enough, but I was standing outside the day-to-day world of work.

He had that lost look that people have when life isn't quite working out how they thought. That look which says that reality isn't meeting up to the picture that they have in their head. It's a vacancy in the eyes, a slight rolling that can be interpreted as offishness. The coarser among us try to sum it up in the horrible phrase, 'My wife doesn't understand me.' But there it is. That phrase. That awful phrase. It was never used, but it haunts this tale, then and now.

The fact is, the lost recognise the lost. The searchers recognise each other. It's the nature of courtship and the cleverness of humans. They don't need many signals to put two and two together. Only this equation was very deceptive. It wasn't two and two, but another calculation entirely. The symptoms were the same although it was a different disease. What's love, anyway? To be in love is to be quite, quite mad. Who said anything about love? When the pop songs ring in your ear, be very, very, very careful. Why did you let me go?

We got closer. He remembered more things, more words, and I remembered how exciting the world was. We nearly left in each other pockets but...

... but it wasn't working out. He was too spaced out. He needed her. He had to stay with her. That's what I saw. I backed away.
I was proud of myself, at the time, I recall, for being so sensible. I don't, often, see myself as a sensible person. Hard-edged perhaps. A bit too sour and sharp for the niceties of polite culture. Was I hard on myself? What kind of mirror was I holding up, a rose-tinted one, or one that showed the worms eating me away from within? Perhaps, I was finally growing up, and realising that dreams didn't come true. You made the best of things. I'd adjusted. We'd all adjusted. We lived with the truth that this was never going to work out. We'd got on with our lives. They were good. Or, they weren't bad.

Now, it seemed, he hadn't lived with that. At all.

'I'm looking for you.'
Yup, that's what he'd said.

He told me, over a pint of beer, why and how he was now, two years later, ready for a relationship. He didn't mention, as he leaned across the table eagerly, the thing that seemed most important. He no longer had to stop mid-sentence and think.
I could tell that a huge thing had happened to him. I couldn't sense what it was, but I had a feeling that I was going to find out very shortly. He was careful and slow. I was sure he'd tell me, but in his own time. We talked about our lives a little, but not much. And music, not much. About the days, how the sun rose and how it set over the hills, in Ireland and the Pennines. I was an Earnshaw. The family that had given birth to Catherine Earnshaw. The moors were in my veins. I knew how the heather grew and how the dog-grass was dry and sharp. He told how, when he was just a little boy, over-adventurous, a wall-walker, he'd fallen into a wide, aggressive field of nettles and hadn't got hurt. A superhuman boy, an enigmatic, strange boy. I jumped from tussock to tussock on the marshes and never twisted my ankle. Sure-footed.
The city was dark and swirled around us like a cloak. We were together.

154

'I've built my own house,' he said.

And told me about it. How he'd worked so hard. On his own. To make his dream come true.

The struggles. The plot of land had been bought at such a high price because of the great crash. Everyone had wanted houses in London. The market had gone crazy and then crashed. He'd bought it at the wrong time.

The self-builders all were a group. Working together. They bought their land together. Each one helped the others build their house.

He took me to see the house he'd built for us.

Tall, brick pointing to the sky, of course. A three-story townhouse, modern, built better than houses were built these days. A kind of anomaly, like his curly hair and my straw locks. Two non-fits.

We walked towards the house. The zebra crossing nearly ran up to the door, like a carpet of welcome. A red carpet, but black-and-white. We went over its stripes and then up the steps. On the right, a green square of grass. Nothing. No gardener in action. Barely mowed. Then the wooden Carolina door. He got his keys out and turned them in the secure Chubb (5-lever) and Yale, and we were in.

Everything was large and pale and white. White painted fresh corridors. I had a hospital feeling. It was fresh and clean like a ward. He said, 'it needs a woman's touch.' Was I really being asked to play the part of a 1950s housewife? I didn't have the clothes. No full skirts, no pinched waists, no pyramid bras.

Into the open-plan kitchen. Mahogany units, chrome handles. The sink looked over at the zebra crossing that we'd just crossed. The round orange-yellow globes flashed, two suns. Shining, shining.

Strange new materials. Sisal floor on a jaunty angle. Low pile grey carpet. White, white walls. The fireplace jutted out a thick stone tongue.

'You can have an open fire there,' he said. It looked impossible. It was too modern, too clean. But the stone was thick and ancient. A slab.

Tall windows from ceiling to floor. Outside, the garden was a pile of rubble. It was tiny.

'This is the smallest plot,' he said, 'for cost. I gave as much ground as possible to the house.

At the back of the yard, the neighbours' house rose high, hemming us in. For privacy, the gardens were built with six-foot wooden fences.

This gave the outdoor space with an oppressive feeling, like an auditorium. Eyes were looking down on us.

Three floors, white and blank, grey carpets. Institutionally perfect and minimalist. Clean as a bell. This was a joke. My room seethed with junk, a sea of words, pictures, musical notes, dreams, T-shirts. Minimalism was an art movement that passed me by like the countryside on a railway train; forever separated by the carriage window.

We talked over coffee. He made a pot. We ate his food. I wasn't eating meat, hadn't for a while, but he'd cooked, so I did. Mashed potatoes and beef stew. I'd stepped back into time, into my own timeline a bit, perhaps, into my parents' generation. Nuclear family. The family are the centre of things. You looked after your own. You were important to your family. And your family were important to you.

Mustn't rush things. Things go so fast, the world goes so fast.

What's happened with you?

I'm not one to talk about my own life too much. I like to listen and join in when I have something to say. I might not start a story at the beginning and keep telling it – I like to hear what's going on and then embellish it – take it somewhere else, chip in, keep improvising.

He had a story, stories, family stories. He was quieter but his stories were settled. Stone of stories. Mine kept changing. They were riverlike, stream stories. I didn't have set pieces.

He rode horses. When he was younger, he'd been a champion showjumper. An Irish showjumping champion. He had no fear, you see. The horses liked that. They trusted him. There was no emotion in him for them to sense. He was full of purpose without hesitation.

He was one of seven, and his nearest sister in age, D—, she was competitive. But he was the better rider. It was just a fact. There was a new horse. Beautiful horse but difficult. D— insisted on riding the horse. But she couldn't control it. It bolted. She ended up cracking her head, in hospital. He told me how this was very frightening for his parents. They blamed him, they didn't blame him. It wasn't his fault. Hard to know how to respond best in these situations. We all do things we regret, things we don't mean, in the inner sanctum of the family.

A boy who never had a problem with riding horses. Why, he didn't mind riding a bike now, even after the accident.? He was a bit bandy-legged. Maybe it was the horses. Maybe he was trying to do too much as a kid. Remember he was the youngest of three brothers. Always trying to keep up, do things that were too big, too clever, too hard for him. You have to when you're a boy at the bottom of the sibling hierarchy.

He sat quietly. Smoking. Staring. Just looking down.

He was at college. He hadn't managed to finish. Left school, gone into building as a labourer with his brother-in-law who had a building business in London. He'd gone back now to study his BSc in Furniture Design at the London College of Furniture on the wild stream of traffic that ploughed into London and out every day. They were designing cutlery. He wanted to be ergonomic, make knives suitable to users with disabilities. He showed me a couple of pieces, prototypes carved out of wood. Smooth to hold. And a photo of the great white shark. His inspiration.

That picture of the great white sat on the IKEA shelf divider like a member of the family. I have a shark tooth. They're frightening, smooth, strong and hard. Bone and calcium. Undersea menace. Cutting edge of a killer. Sharks have small, beady eyes. They pierce with their gimlet stare. Sharks are everywhere. People are predatory.

I like to learn.

I'd be able to help him with his written work. There was one thing that I was good at, or I thought so back then, reading and writing. Maybe I wasn't so good at that, not really. Perhaps what I was good at was doing exams.

I certainly wasn't good at building houses. I sat there in awe, looking around at this amazing place he'd built. Who builds their own house in central London? This was the 1990s and this was the Docklands.

Still the strangest of otherworldly places.

1990s Docklands. Canary. Boom, crash, chunk, changle, drilllllllll. The pile drivers piled into the ground like they were punishing it, all of the night and all of the day. I wrote a blues song about it and still have the cassette with the cartoon cover. All of the night and all of the day.

Building. Building. The construction was coming to the end of the first cycle. The foundations were laid for Canary Wharf and it was growing into its mecca for business, money, workers, people who'd slip in and out on the space-age monorail.

Thunk, drrrr, sprrong. Bash. Every day. Even at this point, the very south, the very west of the Island, on its curve around the sloppy grey

157

Thames, thick and brown. The waves are like soup, pointing, stretching, little mountains. The Thames is as difficult to swim in as it looks. A drowning river, a river that will take out even the best swimmers. Would my head girl have made it across or been carried away by the current? Maybe it doesn't look so far, so difficult, but it is. No wonder it's the choice death of the suicide leapers, although a crinoline has thwarted more than one Victorian, billowing out trapping the air, gliding the woman to safety, a miraculous rebirth. But unless you're blessed, it will take you.

The human body can't fight it. If you end up in that churning slop, girl, you'll drown. Cruel gruel.

'Why don't you move in?' he asked.

No, take it slowly. Be sensible.

'I've finished with D—'

Yes, but I was still with my anarchist boyfriend. We were ticking along. It was fine. Going nowhere slowly, but fine.

Hmmm.

I believed honesty was the best policy.

Is it, is it really? I thought so. Honestly I thought so. I told him everything. That was kind. As kind as I could. You have to be cruel to be kind. I stood in a doorway, I opened my mouth and said some words.

'Sorry'. That was a word I used. Repeatedly.

It's very difficult, to be honest.

To be careful. Before I told my anarchist boyfriend, I first got the housing association to re-house me.

In the end, I never moved in, just dumped my stuff at his house.

That beautiful house by the winding Thames. That modern clean house, with its white walls, so pristine, I would never fit in. My stuff looked odd there. It's fine, he said.

It was summer, and instead we went on holiday on a driving adventure – to France.

At the door, in his slate-grey Alfa Romeo came his friend A—. Chatty, lively. Older. Hippy. Full of the gob, full of philosophy. Moustache, weathered optimism. His parents had made their money in ice-cream in Northern Ireland. And now we were going to drive through France.

Alfa Romeos are a dust bucket. That's what they say. You'll be crying at the side of the road most days of the year.

But they're classic. One day of the year you'll be in heaven.

Especially in the hands of a veteran, car-loving Italian, driving back to Italy.

I had to go back to work, so I was going to fly back from the south of France.

Reaching Dover was easy. No need for navigation. They took it in turns to drive. First stop, first proper stop was the Magic Mountain, just outside Paris. We were now on the side roads. We didn't want to go straight back on the main motorways and it was nice to see things, but the journey was tiring us out. Navigation was a bit difficult, but we had a detailed road map. Crossing junctions, turning left, right, wigging our way through the dirt tracks of this field and that village. S—went to sleep on the back seat. A— and I were left to negotiate.

The back seat was peaceful.

He awoke suddenly and shouted.

'You shouldn't have crossed the bridge!'

We'd gone over the river. How had he managed to sense that in his dreams? How did he know? A— and I laughed, amazed. He was right of course.

He had powers.

This was a time when the Magic Mountain didn't exist. It was being constructed by mates of A—. There was just a large gothic building, green gardens, tall church windows, red-brick. A vast edifice made for the servants of God. A nunnery.

No women allowed! A nunnery with no women allowed. Rows of dorms, all for construction workers from Ireland. From Cavan, from Cork, from Donegal, from Limerick, from Monaghan, from the small villages where the Guinness was hopefully good as that was what you drank. I was smuggled in beneath a blanket of accents from all over Ireland. A cup of tea and chat and then on the road again, letting the lands carry on digging foundations, making generations of children to come, happy. There's hard work behind the glitz and the glitter.

After this, the roads were wide and thick and hard with traffic. It was getting hot. So hot. We stopped by a canal. I didn't have my swimming costume, but I couldn't resist the green water. I slipped in and swam while the boys ate their picnic next to the narrowboats. I lay on my back in the inland water and saw the clouds settled and yawning in the cyan sea above. The sun was hot on my skin which felt fresh with the day.

The hot fields of France baked beneath the summer, but I was cool and cucumber-moist.

I towelled off and ate the baguette and cheese. So many bread flakes, brush them off into the grass.

It's easy to travel with somebody neat who can organise things. You can be free. You can wake up in the morning and stretch your arms into the sun, really feel that this is you and this is the world without any worries.

We reached the town of Montpellier by evening. Jazz town. University town. A huge piazza. Buskers. Rosy sun and a meal of lapin even though I didn't really want to eat rabbit, the sauce, red and thick, was good and salty and this was rural French living. A tagine, a couscous, North Africa had crossed the Mediterranean. The scent of lemons in my bag.

So why don't we get married, he asked. We sat outside a small cafe as the sun got low in the sky. Long days in Montpellier. Anything can happen. A jazz combo started to play. I'd always loved the deep plonk of the double bass. It sounds better in French.

I'd never been interested in getting married. How much had I changed.

Travelling in a smile we parted ways with A— as we met up with family friends in the Camargue. I saw white horses in my dreams, capering and displaying themselves over the marshes, nuzzling tussocks and rearing like a childhood fantasy.

We were walking in the evening through the spooky café landscape of Van Gogh's late paintings, the starry, starry night making arabesques, musical twists. Pop blasting from radios and the chinks of knives and forks on plates.

Stars and stars and stars and stars.

Wild horses must be free.

Winter was cold as always. I always seemed to be at work. One crazy play after another at the arts centre. Drama. It was a centre of drama. Colleagues were arguing, getting jobs, falling around. C— got so stoned in the toilet at work that he'd almost fallen out of the door in a cloud of smoke.

All the actors that were worth their salt got BBC small parts. Everyone worked on The Bill or EastEnders. Some got proper jobs. Like

S— B—. He was going somewhere. It helped that he was absolutely hilarious, especially when he told stories about his lazy uncle, or did impersonations behind closed doors. I knew he must do me. I used to hide around the corner and look through the door in the hope that he might do me one day, but I never saw it.

However much fun work was, I always looked forward to going home.

When I got in, home never seemed to live up to its promise. There was something on his mind. If only I knew what it was!

He sat at that round table in his carefully, elegantly, contemporary designed kitchen. I sat with him. He looked thoughtful. If only he could say what was bothering him. His pale blue eyes were so sad. Speak to me! Perhaps he just needed to feel more secure.

I asked other people what might be the matter. He just needs to feel more secure, said friends who saw us together. It's obvious that you two are made for each other. You can see it in your eyes, just how much you're in love.

There was a story he told about the self-build. One man had been ripping the others off. It was a strange story. He was keeping a file on him.

'Oh, don't worry about that,' I said. 'We're all right.'

He put the file away, but it was preying on him, I could see. He was a lot in debt. It was an odd story about which I knew nothing, apart from it wasn't relevant anymore.

'Leave it,' I said, 'everything's okay, just give it time.'

I could understand why it was a big pressure, financial problems are highly stressful. They drive people to suicide. Boom and bust was all around us. This was the Isle of Dogs. Every day I heard about some city banker or dealer that went AWOL and ended up jumping or on the other side of the world. The great crash had taken many victims. We lived in its aftermath.

'Don't worry about that,' I said. I still hoped we could go and live in the Irish countryside at some point. I fancied myself in a pair of wellies, stomping around a muddy field with a couple of sheep. I never was much of a city slicker.

You'll get mud stress, they said, don't do it.

Getting married is so much fun that I recommend it. The show is the most beautiful thing. Your ego at the centre of your friends and family. The planning. The cool party. Beautiful bouquets, fun clothes without worrying about how much you spend because there'll always be people who spend way more on their weddings than you can. A huge event with you at the centre. Gifts. Everyone wishing you well for the future. A symbol that you've finally grown up.

There was this beautiful flower shop in Covent Garden. I'd always wanted rosemary and lavender and grasses and beautiful anemones, and I had the loveliest bouquet. It had been born from the lifestyle supplement in The Observer. A designer bouquet. Swinging London style, but purple and blue, lavender, grasses. Except it was huge. I asked them to change it. They were upset. But it's too big, I told them. They weren't impressed, they had done their best. But it was too wide for my hands. Their disappointment made me sad too. It cast a cloud on my bouquet choice.

Never mind. These things really don't matter, they don't.

A friend made an Elizabethan style dress with beads out of Thai silk. Other friends played, saxophone and keyboard. We were the last two to get married in a church on the Isle of Dogs that now is knocked down. Another friend took beautiful black and white photos. I've thrown them all away. I've ripped them up. Sorry friends. I let you down.

It's embarrassing.

We went to Fethiye, Turkey for our honeymoon. Tales of turtles hatching. Cave buildings, ancient as Neanderthal, ancient as Jurassic, ancient as the Old Testament. Bluer sky than I'd ever seen before.

Let's go north to the caves. How shall we get there?

I insisted we hire a boat, a fisherman would take us over in his little motor. We went north over the lake, up and down on the waves. In the middle. Nothing. A Plate of water. Level. Then mountains of water. You couldn't see the bank. Up and down. I wasn't sick but I was scared. I hid in the bottom of the boat, lay down, felt it reel from side to side, pretended I wasn't bothered. A crazy massage.

We went north to the salt pools, where you can swim in the thermals over the remains of a marble-white Greek temple.

But at night things weren't right already. I covered the darkness with Sellotape. What was it all about?

During the day, Turkish men chatted me up, but I wasn't available.

They wouldn't believe it until I showed them our matching platinum rings. Surely I didn't look that young.

Okay, we believe you.

On the bus, a young man sat next to me was friendly. So keen to tell me how he too loved Irish music. Chris de Burgh.

Fethiye was a universe I wouldn't go back to. I was glad to get home. Perhaps things would be less stressful for him there. Something was freaking him out.

At home I fancied learning to ride, so off I went to our local city farm, Mudchute. One of the most beautiful things about the Isle of Dogs, I thought, were the wonderful, large city farms. See smelly old pigs! Commune with sheep! Walk on the grassy fields with the animals, the cityscape on the skyline. And have another go at learning to ride. I got to canter. A horsey smell on my hands, the hairs, the thick scratchy mane like a doll's hair.

But I wasn't feeling so well. Bit sick. My skin wasn't right. It was terribly itchy. I had to scratch it. It was beginning to flake like my old eczema was coming back. Was it stress? I didn't feel stressed, I felt powerful and young.

I went to a Chinese herbalist who knocked me up some horrible bitter concoction, full of powder. She said my balance wasn't right.

But I was sick. Every morning. Finally, the penny dropped.

Ah, the blue stripe of the pregnancy test.

Oh.

Well, well. Here we are at another life-changing, life-enhancing, life-expectant moment. Landmark.

Pregnancy. There's nothing like it for saying nothing will ever be the same again. Unless you turn around. But I wasn't going to. I knew this was the one. It was time. The bells were ringing inside my head. My clock was chiming in my ear louder than Big Ben.

I walked around in circles, thinking, letting my thoughts roar like a train. I couldn't hear anything for these inner sounds. This was it. This would calm him down. Now he could feel secure and he need not worry anymore. Now we were together forever and that would make him happy.

He went outside and gathered the most beautiful bunch of flowers from the trees. Lilacs and wildflowers, grasses. He placed them in a cool glass IKEA vase on the television. Happy news. Happy flowers.

'I don't want to do the garden,' he'd said, 'that's for you.'
I loved gardening.
'I need a gardener.'
Doesn't everyone like gardening?
'Not my thing.'
'It is mine.'
He went into the back and stroked his chin and thought. No good.
This is just rubble. He collected some odd paving slabs. And some railway
sleepers. And began to build a crazy paving base. Quietly crouching,
carefully laying sand, laying slabs on sand. Arranging them neatly.
Stepping back, taking stock. Stepping forward. Laying them. The railway
sleepers he erected at odd angles in terraces that climbed up the three
fences at the back. Artistic beds to take the plants. Coppery fennel on
every side began to grow, seeded itself everywhere, like hair that's out of
control. The smell of fennel was everywhere that summer. Hot fennel.
Lady copper-fringe herb.

Arranging objects on the mantlepiece. Worried. Worried. They
have to go in this order. They must. Don't touch them.
I won't touch them. That's okay. They look good like that.
They HAVE to go in this order.
Okay.

The evenings grew dark and he grew more worried. He'd sit in the
darkness. I'd surprise him when I turned on the light.

We went to Cambridge for a day out. He couldn't cross over the
doorways. He had to stay on the other side. We went home.
Come on it's fine.
No, I'll stay here.
Nothing could make him relax.

I rarely cook. I'm not a great cook. I made meatballs. With herbs. I
spent a long time on them. For me. Meatballs with herbs in tomato sauce.
Exactly the kind of thing he liked.
He wouldn't eat them. He pushed them around his plate with a

fork.

ARE YOU TRYING TO POISON ME?

ARE YOU TRYING TO POISON ME!

He stood up and pushed his chair back.

No, not at all. No. I'm not. Why would you think that?

What do you say when someone accuses you of trying to poison them?

Do you cry, or do you just get great big eyes where the tears stay behind?

At work – yes, things are great. Smiling. I'm so happy. Let's get this maternity leave organised. I want to work as long as I can.

There's something missing.

I'm empty.

He could tell it wasn't right.

He knew I was sad.

We were, after all, still in love.

One evening he turned up with a hairy dog. Cute. He saw an advert in LOOT. 'Small friendly dog. Home needed.' Went and got her. A cute brown raggedy lurcher. HOOCH. Two fudge eyes and a chocolate nose. Hello. Hey, oh wow. Such a sweet dog, so keen to please, so keen to be my friend. Scruffy. The best dogs are scruffy. They just know you. You don't have to tell them to sit to stand to stay to run to eat to not eat. If you do, they'll try and please. They're yours. She'd be with me, full of life. I had a dog. He'd got me a dog.

Oh, my goodness she could run. She was the fastest dog on the block. Wheeeeeeeee around you in circles. But she never, never let you out of her sight.

He finally worked out what the problem was.

His mother, he said, must have had an affair so he wasn't his father's son.

But you look, I said, just like your father. You had an incredibly strong bond with your father. You nursed him through his bowel cancer. You've told me about it. That must have been incredibly stressful. I wish I could've been there.

No, he said, there's something wrong. I don't know what it is, but something's wrong. I need to find out.

Well, I don't know, I said, how could I know. You'll have to ask your family. You'll have to ask them about it. It's not something I could possibly know anything about.

Then he started writing letters.

There were whole conspiracies that started.

Accusations and claims and suppositions.

The law isn't for me.

His uncle, a famous poet, had never really got on with his mother. He decided that the uncle must be his father. He wrote to him about it. Uncle J— sent back a kind letter, saying he couldn't understand where he'd got the idea from, but that, as S— was clearly missing his father, he'd step in and be a father figure for him if he wanted.

Uncle J— lived far away in Cork. I never met him, which was a real shame. I did see a film with him and John Boorman at the BFI film festival. There he was. It was nice to see his face and his life in the hills of Wicklow. It's a beautiful place to live.

Once, S— and I went driving through those hills. We drove through those one-horse towns, those small villages, popped into tiny shops, felt free and easy. It was a beautiful drive. Meandering. Hilly. Free.

His other ideas fixated on computers. There was a successful company called Symantec that was producing software for the evolving Macs. He decided that Symantec was his company to inherit. That it should be his. He concocted a whole theory that hurt my head.

I didn't know what to do.

Denial is a great thing. You can lose your mind without it. Put your nose to a dog and smell its earthy smell. Look into those chewy eyes and see your face reflected. There's a big soft tongue that will lick you. People and their awful social problems don't exist in the eyes of a dog. Let them be free near you, move around, be happy. Dogs smell of dog.

How many times had I begged for a dog as a child. Never, never had I had one. Yes, it was probably for the best, but it hurt me so much not to have one.

Having a dog was just as wonderful as I'd imagined.

But it wasn't so good when you went outside. This dog didn't like to be left alone. She went crazy. Fortunately S—, at least, was at home a lot as he wasn't working.

We left it alone one day. Only for a couple of hours. It went mad.

It got itself stuff in the bedroom and got its paws, it's claw-sharp, scrabbling, claw-pouncing paws on S—'s old silk dressing gown. It managed, magically, to rip it up into tiny squares! Those squares of old paisley silk, spinning and falling everywhere. Impossibly indoor snow.

Fortunately, we had a garden, a yard where we could leave it. We went out with confidence. We'll only be an hour – or two. When we came back with the shopping, it was running around up and down the street. How did it do that? Magic dog.

Only tiny, she'd managed to clear the six-foot fences from a standstill.

Incredible, athletic, spritely, jumping Hooch!

Brilliant, dynamic, springing, brilliant Hooch!

Tremendous, charming, ridiculous, animated Hooch!

Troublesome, worrying, difficult, impossible Hooch!

The stories were preying on him like a succubus.

It was obviously because he'd been brought up in Northern Ireland during the troubles. It was all the fault of the British government. It was all the fault of the army. Everyone grew up with stories about houses being bugged. Friends had their doors kicked in during the middle of the night. Woke up to screams of their mother as their father was dragged out of bed.

His father was a lawyer. A lawyer who looked after the cases of the arrested. How many tearful, screaming mothers would turn up at his house in the middle of the night to cry, 'They've taken him off! He's been taken to the ... ' The tears, the tears. 'They've taken him away, down to the ... ' The raised voices would wake up the children. There'd be cups of tea on the farmhouse kitchen. There'd be phone calls and phone calls. Forms filled in. Scribblings and worryings in the middle of the darkest hours when a child needs to sleep to get ready for school. While his mother needed to prepare for work at the pharmacy.

He crept downstairs, sat on the steps and listened.

The bombs exploding all around his adolescence. This town, that town. His secondary school in Omagh, now remembered for the shopping bomb, shattered glass. Only a small place. A friendly place full of friendly people. Mostly Catholics. This was a Catholic area full of people like his family, although his family considered themselves rather the elite of the area, he said. His girlfriend had been thrilled to go out with a son of 'the house on the hill'.

The Montagues. Three brothers. Magic number three. Seamus, the doctor, Turlough the lawyer and John the poet. There was a story of three brothers, back in the past, who came from France to Ireland. These three brothers settled there and became Irish.

SOMEONE'S BUGGING THIS HOUSE.

I never really knew anymore how much of what came out of his mouth was fact and how much was fiction. Who knows what is the real truth? I like stories. I can live in a land of stories.

But then, it depends on the stories.

When the stories are frightening, paranoid, and accuse those around you... when they focus on people you meet... friends and loved ones... the targets shifted closer and closer. It was only a matter of time before they landed on me... fixed on me... and I'd never be able to get out of the net that had trapped me.

YOU'RE BEING WATCHED

YES YOU

YOU, READING THIS BOOK

I was determined not to think about it.

DENIAL. It's very, very, very useful. It's a kind of magic spell.

You make it by turning around three times dead fast and waving bay leaves over the kitchen stove.

But it only lasts so long. And when it wears off, well... it begins to rub off pretty quickly.

WHO ARE YOU?

You know who you are. I'm me. But I'm not sure who you are anymore.

I was sleeping soundly, dreaming about happiness. I woke up. He was pacing up and down so fast. All night he'd walk and walk and walk.

'I never sleep longer than 4.30 a.m. then my stomach turns inside out. It fires up like a blowtorch. Maybe it's the fear of not being good enough,' said Ingmar Bergman. He was a perfectionist.

My husband was Ingmar Bergman. He was pounding the carpet, wearing it out. He was black-and-white. I was a paper puppet in the theatre. It wasn't a comedy.

I turned over. Unsettled.

I presume he was sleeping during the day. Or was he? I was at work.

It's hard to work when you're very pregnant but I so didn't care. I wanted as much money as possible, push what I could get from maternity leave to the limits. I had a feeling I'd need as much leeway as I could engineer.

My baby was due in January. I'm a January baby. Born on January 15th. Famously in our family, my one brother and I were born on exactly the same day. Both Capricorn. Our uncle H— was also born on that day. Three years separating M— and I. Both very different but similar. But birthdays were always different from other people's birthdays. Both came directly after Christmas and on the same day. My parents could be accused of bad planning, but we didn't do accusations in our family. We liked to let people be what they were without interference. We were more interested in whatever we were into. Our subjects. Academia. Film. Music. We weren't interested in delving into the inner lives of others and passing judgement on them. Gossip wasn't our thing.

As a child I told my mother that I, not I, I wouldn't let a child suffer by being born straight after Christmas. And that's when my baby was due, at the turn of the year in early January.

I was born in the snow, in the cold snap, when Manchester froze. On a Wednesday. Sad and freezing and cold when the world had stopped.

My own child would be born in the dead heart of winter.

I'd got it wrong. Sadness comes to those born in the snow.

Which meant that it was coming up to Christmas. Pantomimes! One of the busiest times for an arts centre. January would be dead. I was rolling it up to the end and going to leave just before the Christmas shows. Let January hang. No one went out in January. That month was dead as a doornail for theatres.

I have a memory of driving around in my red Lada Samara that my dad had given us for the wedding. A rubbishy old car but it was fine. It let the rain in, so my feet were always wet. I went to pick up the leaflets from a bad-tempered printer who shouted at me down the phone that I had to pick them up – I can't remember the details. There must have been some reason this escalated. There was often stress around the printing of leaflets. Dates, times, something had to be changed last minute. And when I turned up in person and that printer, wrinkled by years bent over the litho machine, suntanned in Spain and hardened by years working in the poor band circling the edge of the city of London, saw how pregnant I was his face drained. All the colour left his face. He couldn't believe he'd pressurised me to turn up in person to pick up the leaflets.

You should have told me, he kept saying over and over again.

I went blank. It wasn't worth saying things. I don't like to defend myself.

Defending yourself, you can turn aggressive. At what point does it change? I can hear his voice still, see him there, his visible anguish, his horror that he'd violated, unwittingly, his own moral code about family, about women, about the domestic world being the most important of all. You should have told me.
You should have told me.

Over Christmas I spent it quietly at the house I remember, getting ready. We were peaceful. Angels singing in my mind.

Holy, holy, holy.

Christmas is the time to have a baby. It's all about giving birth. I was going to have my baby at home. I'd decided it was going to happen in the bathroom.

The bathroom. A beautiful, huge bathroom at the front. Lights that shone over the walls as cars went past, tracked across the ceiling and walls as if searching for bombers in wartime London. Everything was so large for me in that house. I was going to have the baby in the bath. The bath was enormous, I couldn't push myself with my feet easily off the bottom which was my habit. That irritated my body as it couldn't indulge in its usual physical tricks, the ones it relied on for my brain to enter its comfortable, automatic zone.

I was going to have a home birth. This was the gynaecological territory of Wendy Savage, the famous pro-choice doctor. And I'd have my first baby at home.

Dangerous! Bad choice!

No, I still think no, and why? I was really close to the hospital if anything went wrong. And I had great midwives monitoring my birth. My pregnancy was uncomplicated. I had taken the huge torpedo iron tablets.

I wanted a water birth, but it seemed ridiculous to hire a pool when I had this huge bath. Also unnecessary. Showy. A little odd, really. It wasn't a theatre show. Didn't feel right. And we needed to be economical with money. He wasn't working. Still hadn't worked, done any work at all. And I was about to go on maternity leave. And the way he was behaving I really wasn't sure if I was going to be leaving the baby with him. When the baby came. Money was important.

But it was important to have fun as well. I went singing karaoke.

I went for dinner as well in a Thai restaurant in Islington. With friends. It felt like D-Day. Big mistake. I should have been home. Like my mum would've been.

Someone said something and I ended up vomiting my food right back on my plate. It re-emerged, replacing the food I had eaten.

I was glad that the restaurant was dark.

I was sorry for the restaurant owners and staff.

Mostly I was so embarrassed.

The low light. The good restaurant. The kind waitress. The plate, left lonely on the table, full of vomit-soup.

It was early morning on January 3rd. I broke inside. The waters came down. Oh, my goodness. This beautiful, pale, watery fluid, like the clearest crystal river. I didn't know it would be so pure. Fonte chiara.

The water poured over me, down my legs, onto the floor. There was so much of it. It broke like a balloon being popped and the water was everywhere. It soaked me, it soaked the carpet. It was incredible. And then the baby started to move.

How do you prepare for pain? I'm often quite good with pain. I can cope with difficulties.

'You didn't tell me,' said my husband's sister to his mother, 'that it would be so painful,' when she sat in hospital after her first baby.

'Of course not,' said her mother, 'how could I tell you? For what good?'

Or something like that. Being from a large family full of sisters as well as brothers, my husband had more stories than me of birth, of children, he was full of overheard, retold, the fixed tales that are told time and time again and that have stuck in someone's mind and gone round and round the group.

I had magazines, novels, television, textbooks, friends. But none of my friends had had babies. They were intellectual women and none of them were ready to give birth anytime soon. They were lawyers, writers, novelists, dreamers, thinkers, artists, actors, dropouts, wannabes and many of them were men. They were all away from home in a different country that is London for an immigrant like me, an immigrant from the regions, an economic migrant from the small towns around Manchester. They're falling down in post-industrial decline. Run, to the capital! That's what I'd done. And my friends were Spanish, Italian, French, Irish, Scottish, American, Korean, Moroccan, Ghanaian, Zimbabwean, South African... we were away from home and making it good or bad in a city without family but full of work.

I had hired a TENS machine, to give myself electric shocks and somehow get rid of the pains of the contractions. There was nitrous oxide in a gas cylinder ready in the bathroom. But apart from that, I wasn't going to have anything. It was worth it to give birth at home.

I was so nervous. I couldn't relax. I phoned the midwife.

Go for a walk, take it easy, have something light to eat – a cheese sandwich? – a cup of tea? – I went for a walk with the dog and S— over the football field. I walked round and round in the cold misty air. We walked anticlockwise. The light was white-grey. There was no one else there. It was him, me and Hooch. Everyone else in the world had vanished. Such stillness. Perhaps there were ghosts gathered around the edge of the field, ancestors staring at me, watching me.

I'd be glad not to be pregnant anymore. I just wanted it out of me. Get it out!

My body was getting ready to get it out?

I knew the baby had turned well, baby's heels now over baby's head, and we were ready to go. How fast would it happen? How many hours? 8 hours? 12 hours? 16? 24? The numbers hummed in my head. So many hours in labour. How long would I be in labour? Those numbers frightened me. They swam huge and small, it seemed impossibly long to be in pain.

There's no going back. Pregnancy and birth, this tunnel that you enter so blithely and the longer you stay the narrower it becomes. There's only one way out, you have to squeeze yourself through the chink of light at the end. But it's so small, so tiny that only you can push yourself out there. You're alone with the walls of the tunnel.

It's a canal tunnel and you're sailing along the waters, pushing yourself towards it. When you get through there'll be a huge cry and a shout in the sunshine.

It's as though I was giving birth to myself.

You're not ready, the midwife told me. I'm going to go away. After checking me. Call me if there's a problem.

I didn't blame her for not wanting to hang out. She was right. Baby didn't come until the early morning.

He's definitely a boy I said. We'd been saying this all along. We were convinced he was a little boy, he was so fast and quick in the ultrasound, a fish, full of energy, scooting around there, zipping with zip. Later on, he'd kicked me in the ribs repeatedly. Always in the same rib on the left. I can feel it now, the kicks, the dull thud against my ribs from the inside. Bang, bang, bang. A dull pain, like a mallet. It rocked and annoyed like a stitch.

Whenever I lay down, I could feel him kicking me. Kick kick kick. Wake up Mum, smell the coffee.

You're holding it in, said the midwife. Sarah, Susan. Sorry, can't remember your name. You were all brilliant. When I was having the worst period pains ever. It seems that was what period pains were for, having babies.

The TENS machine was thrown away quickly. It was pretty good at giving you odd contractions. The electricity pulsing through you. More for recreation than anything else.

But she wasn't. A boy.

I was in the bath. The last stages. I felt the change.

'You can't have any more gas,' said the midwife.

He??? was silent, tense.

Strangely everything seemed as natural as the moon.

She came out beautifully. In the early hours.

What is she? She's lovely.

She. A girl, like me.

She'd been living inside me. She'd been warm in there with the blood.

Towards the end, I came out of the bath to give birth for the last moments.

'Take your time,' the midwife said. 'Now, take your time.'

Hold your breath, pause.

In the end, a little rip. Only a little one. The sharp sting of the rip. Then she arrived. Perfect. Shouting, doing everything right.

Who are you?

WHO ARE YOU?

We love you, little girl. You've arrived in perfect time to get the best out of life. We're prepared for you. We've built a house for you. We've made out lives ready for you.

The claret placenta slopped into a plastic bowl. It slumped there like a lot of liver bought from the supermarket. It looked full of haemoglobin. Pumped nicely with oxygen. Deep dark red. Wine-dark. Burgundy. I stared at the fresh meat for so long. It was fascinating.

A baby was more fascinating.

It came from the sea inside my stomach. The Little Mermaid. Isn't she lucky?

That baby, my baby did things perfectly right from the start. She breastfed by instinct. She knew just how to do what she had to do to stay alive. She was full of beans. I was terrified of killing her, but she knew how to look after herself.

The dog too was good. I'd heard that dogs could be jealous, but Hooch sat on the staircase through the whole business, quiet as a lamb. Careful to be around us all the time but to keep out of the way. Do dogs, sensitive dogs like Hooch, have an ability to sense what's going on at such moments? Why not? This is part of their natural lives in the wolf-pack. Ancestral instinct, ancestral memory must kick in. She sat on the square bit on the stairs where the corner turned, awake, alert, ears at half-mast, but quiet and relaxing.   The atmosphere was quietly tense but not dangerous.

It was the adult world, the people that were about to let me down. The dog was innocent.

The dreams had been going on for weeks. Waking up in the middle of the night. I had stopped asking him if he was okay. I didn't like the conversations. I just wanted things to be quiet. I needed to live in denial. There was too much else to think about. I didn't have time to deal with his ridiculous, non-essential problems. I had to focus on having a baby.

It wasn't as if I knew a lot about having a baby. I was the youngest of two. I only had an older brother. I had no experience of looking after small children. I had no sisters to step in and hold me by the hand and show me the way. No friends with babies that I was close to – and when you're in a house of erratic, movable emotions – of unpredictable stories and reactions – your friends soon part ways with you. They disperse. And you're left alone. And you don't want them there, if you're private. You don't want them to see the mess under the surface. You don't want to confess the things that are troubling you. You want to keep them in a black box in your mind. That's where they live, in the toy chest at the back. Stuff them in there, ready to pop back up when opened like an evil jack-in-the-box. Boinnnnggg! I'm here! Boinnnnggg!

That first night we slept, it was fine. OR did we. I did. Or was it okay? Was this a dream? I couldn't be a mother. Maybe it was a few days later when I woke up in the thin hours to find myself inside his dream.

Who are you?

WHO ARE YOU?

And an arm flew across.

I got a black eye for a birthday present.

I had never had a black eye before. It's impossible to disguise them however much makeup you use. Bruising on the face is incredibly hard to live with. You can't look at yourself in the mirror. It's odd. Is that you? Are you a battered wife?

But I have to stay here. This is the house she was born into, her birthright. It belongs to her. This is her nest.

And a mother and a baby are the same person. Only a few days ago

175

this was literally true. It's still true. We're only separated by a bit of air. The mechanics have changed, she's now breastfeeding, but we're the same person. We're together every moment of the day. She's sleeping. She could be sleeping inside me. Instead, she's in a cot by the side of my bed. She can see me through the bars. She looks into my eyes and I look into hers. She has blue eyes. I do too. He has blue eyes as well. The blue-eyed family. Six blue eyes staring in different directions with different expressions.

There were many different midwives, all blonde, all slightly interchangeable. One noticed the black eye and wrote it in the little pink book.

I asked another to take it out. She took it out.

I was terrified of social workers. What could I do?

The walls were starting to close in.

Probably I should have gone home to my own mother, she'd take care of me. You could rely on her. Why didn't I? Perhaps I was a fool. A stubborn fool.

Perhaps he was suffering from some kind of trauma because of the marriage, pregnancy and birth happening too fast. What I did manage to do was get him to the doctor's.

Hello, Doctor. Can you look at my husband and talk to him.

Of course, you can't go in. You're excluded. That's how it works.

I sat outside with the baby while he talked.

The doctor saw him.

He was my hero.

My husband, the hero.

We bumbled along.

Breast turned into bottle, naturally.

She hung in a bouncing chair off the door. She loved it, turning from side to side to look at everything. Hyperactive child.

He changed nappies well but couldn't concentrate on looking after the baby. He was too busy accusing his family of not being his family. I wouldn't read the letters.

Each day he was spending more time looking at the round table. It shone like a huge indoor moon, back in his face. His conversations were less and less reliable.

He frightened me. I went walking with the baby to the park in the rain. It was me, the rain, the dog and the baby, on the Isle of Dogs.

Some days, a little bit of clarity kicked in and we seemed almost normal. On these days he liked to drive and do errands. We went to IKEA, collecting things for the family. There always seemed to be a list of what people wanted.

Why was that a good day out, buying flat-packed furniture, rugs and soft toys. I bought a mouse and a snake that could curl around the stairs. And a fox.

Foxy! Foxy would be a favourite.

On our rare day out, we went into the IKEA restaurant. Swedish meatballs and lingonberry sauce. It was a canteen where the furniture, the highchairs, were the same as we had at home. The sound of conversation, middle-class families eating and talking about 'normality' ricocheted around the store restaurant.

When we returned to the car, it looked like a snow globe with a bouncing, rocketing creature at the heart. Hooch had gone mad being left alone in the car and had ripped all the nappies into floating snowflakes. They whirled around the jumping dog.

You haven't lived until you've seen a red Lada Samara turn into a living snow globe.

Hooch, it's okay!

Hooch, calm down, we're back. The three of us, your family.

Battersea Dogs' Home code – DWLA means Destructive When Left Alone.

I was told that.

Foxy was a favourite straight away, with Foxy's furry tail and cute eyes. But nothing would ever beat Bunny. Bunny had been one of her earliest gifts. She would always carry it with her.

Shaking the bed, in the middle of the night, WHO ARE YOU?

I asked his best friend from Ireland, whom I knew, who was a mental health nurse and who had known him for years, what was going on and what I should do. He said, 'We have to believe him'.

But he didn't believe me. He just wouldn't tell me not to believe him. He told me to believe him.

I don't know if he was being a friend, a mental health nurse, or what, but he wasn't helpful to me. It was up to me. He was letting me sink or swim in my own boat. Like a fool, I insisted on him paddling that boat. Hero or martyr, I played that role.

A gigantic cat reached over and took me up, held me gently in its mouth. It might eat me at any moment. I was in bed on its tongue. I was in mortal danger. The sound of laughing. I woke up to find her laughing at me. She rarely cried.

As the scenarios escalated, the nights broke apart more and more, and my home life was starting to remind me of key speeches in Macbeth, 'Macbeth hath murdered sleep!' The doctor suggested hospital. The best thing, she said, would be for him to self-hospitalise, to voluntarily section himself and go into the Rachel Ward at the London Hospital. Then they could assess him, give him a proper course of medication and deal with it properly.

Okay.

He agreed.

He was tired of the nightmare scenarios.

And we stopped trying to manage at home. The might of the NHS was on our side. Surely everything wouldn't be okay. I'd been right not to give up too early. I'd been right!

I didn't need Tarot cards to predict my situation. I didn't need my friends to tell me what they'd do if they were in my shoes. I found myself unable to describe what was happening to them and I couldn't find a way of making it fit into normal conversation, it felt too bizarre. Now I had medical professionals on my side. I could only talk to people who knew him, to his family and his friends, and they hadn't helped me. They just started to clam up, or even get aggressive, even though I wasn't hostile, but I was saying things they didn't want to hear. And they were angry about his accusations. I got the blame for them in some way, even though I had never repeated any, not even to my family. I never really believed them. And my family were never interested in gossip.

When I saw mental health hospitals in the media, when I read books about them, they were always bad. Sylvia Plath went into hospital and signed herself up for electro-convulsive therapy. She wrote eloquently about her experience in The Bell Jar. She had two operations, which she remembered very differently. The description of one is chilling and frightens.

The other was 'One Flew Over the Cuckoo's Nest'. Jack Nicholson versus the Nurse. She's a devil, a controller. Society versus the individual. She wins. His rebellious grin is reduced by an operation to dumb, inane compliance. His personality is murdered. In the end, the large, native American inmate breaks out by ripping up the water fountain, smashing the window and running free.

Many women, in particular, I had been told, went into mental health wards and never came out. My friend Jill was a mental health nurse and looked after many elderly women who had become institutionalised but who never should have been kept in what they used to call lunatic asylums. Such institutions were being shut, up and down the country at this time, with good reason. They were the years of the government policy, 'Care in the Community'. It was rolling out all over me, and into me. I guess my little family were rolling the other way. We needed help.

I left the baby at the childminder. Bye, bye darling, have a lovely time with all your new friends. She turned around and crawled straight for the tower that the group were building. Not a single tear or look back. It was like she was already leaving home. Took after me, I guess, independent from day one. I was proud of her. It made me smile.

Then I went to the hospital with him.

The ward was on the top floor overlooking Whitechapel High Street. There, a bunch of men who found it difficult to cope in their everyday lives and needed medication to get them back on a mental platform were living with each other, supervised by nurses, over-supervised by the consultants and the high-up personnel. It's still a mystery to me, the world of trolleys and flip charts and bottles of pills, rattling and rattling with their long Latinate names. To immerse your thoughts in what drugs do to the mind, the latest drugs, what they block and what they stimulate. It's another world to recreational drug use, which started to seem simple in comparison, naïve, all about floating colours and staying up all night to have a good time, to make the party never end.

Come on, take me higher.

You couldn't get any higher than the Rachel Ward. We'd reached the top.

I was told by someone, I think a nurse, that most of the treatment was chemical here, that they'd give him high dosages and then wean him off gradually until he stabilised. Dosage was at the heart of the treatment. They'd watch him and talk to him and they'd see how things went, how he behaved, what he said and what was going on in his mind, as best they could.

Meantime I had to get on with stuff.

It was just me and the baby.

I put on records and danced around the flat. Jumping over the diagonal that separated the kitchen from the open-plan room. Records I'd found in charity shops. My few records that nestled between the Saw Doctors and the Chieftains, between the punk and the Irish songsters. My traditional Irish music (diddle-dee-dee music to him and his sisters growing up, they'd looked down on it as children, but he'd recently discovered Davy Spillane) and my African music collection, thin but really valued. The B52s and the battered charity-shop Everly Brothers.

She found my dancing hilarious. Who would've thought that flinging an arm and a leg here and there could be so amusing.

The funniest was when I waxed my legs. She found the action as the strip removed the hairs, the sound and the rasp of the pull, hilarious. Each time – HA HA HA HA HA!

For me, my secret vice was baby shoes. I loved them. The little shoelaces. The tiny boots. The miniature straps and buckles, eyelets and punched holes. I could look at them and hold them for hours. And baby feet, plump and sweet like pale berries.

But strange, as baby feet don't need shoes. We play at making our babies miniature children with shoes that they don't need.

You can leave your baby with a childminder when you pay, but can you leave a DWLA dog alone? No. Try the garden again.

She soared over that six-foot fence like an Olympic athlete. She had the clearance of a pole jumper.

Knock knock.

It's the dog catcher.

Here she is. If she's out on the street again, I'll take her to the pound and she'll be destroyed.

No smiles, this is serious.

I assure, never again.

The dog catcher stands with the zebra crossing behind her, winking and winking at me.

Ha ha, now you're scuppered. How are you going to get out of this one?
What can I do?

You can leave your baby with a childminder but it's not satisfactory. It's not what you want to do. You'd much prefer to stay at home with the baby, bring her up yourself, spend as much time with her as you can. Which is when you discover that bad decisions, bad luck, bad accidents, a lack of health, a lack of mental health impact on family life, impact on everyone around the person who lacks good mental health, including the children, the spouse, the parents, everyone... even the dog.

By this time, I had to tell my parents that he wasn't well and was in hospital. They knew. I liked to manage on my own, but they came down to help me.

No, I wasn't managing with the dog either.

My dad loved that dog.

He sat in the kitchen, at the round table, feeding the dog scraps from his plate.

'Don't do that,' I said, 'We never do that.'
S—'s rules were farm rules. He presented his day-to-day approach to animals as being that of the Irish rural homestead. Country rules. I liked the country. Would I really have been happy on a farm in rural Ireland or was it an illusion?

Mud stress they called it. You could get it in your Wellingtons in the muddy fields of Tipperary.

'What's the point,' said my dad, 'of having a dog if you don't spoil it?' He fed it more scraps, looking into its eyes. 'Good girl,' he said. 'Who's a good little girl? Who's my favourite girl?'

The dog had to go. My dad put an advert in the Manchester LOOT and took Hooch north. He reported seeing her with a new family. He waited around in the car, keeping an eye on how it might go. And he saw the dog with her family, containing children with blissful faces, happily walking with them across a wasteland patch.

Goodbye Hooch. Good luck to you. Good luck to your new family.

Hooch, my first dog. Would you be my last? It was nothing I could worry about now. My life couldn't allow me to be sentimental about you.

Visits to the hospital were quite frightening. I'm not the most social person, I don't consider myself a great success socially. I have so many fears. Not only what it might be like to step off a white concrete box into oblivion and disappear by falling.

I'm made nervous by people I see on the bus. By coats, by bags, by scarves, by hairstyles. By smells. By the way someone moves their arms. By people on the tube trains. By passers-by and doctors and nurses, by teachers and students and rude girls I meet on the street. By soldiers and officers, police and those with no badges to say what they are. By old women with nothing better to do than poke their nose in my business. By their auras, they crackle with electricity. By posters for things I don't want, bare flesh of sexy young women, hyper-realistic food. By old men who have opinions about you and who don't listen to a word you say. By seats that might have germs woven into the upholstery. By young men who look on any woman of over twenty-five as over the hill. By large dogs with long bristling hair. By young men who look on every woman as a sexual possibility, and rate you with their eyes. I'm nervous of the human race, of all my fellows. I know I should be kind and calm and generous. But most of the time I'm too busy simply feeling nervous.

I like to spend a great deal of time on my own. Drawing. Writing. Thinking. Playing music. Staring through the window, looking into the distance, dreaming up scenes, stories, colours and characters. Failing that, I like to spend time with people I know well and trust. Who I know won't attack me for some unwitting mistake, or something absurd that I suddenly do. I find my fellow artists are good company as they relish rather than deride eccentricity.

There's nothing for it. No one else can go instead of me. So I have to go to the hospital, walk through those swinging doors with my heart pounding, my eyes alive and wide. I have to go up those cold hospital steps, floor by floor, onto the top ward of the London Hospital.

I have to walk along to the Men's Ward, to the mental health ward, into the Rachel Ward. See my husband during visiting hours.

When the mind breaks down, says the consultant, it breaks down in predictable ways. But these are different depending on your personality. I've thought about that ever since that day.

Today we sit together in the visiting room.

He shows me photographs he has taken of the busy Whitechapel High Street, with its stalls selling saris, fish, costume jewellery, fruit and vegetables, with its cars racing up and down. It's washed-out, grey and overcast.

'Look,' he says, 'I've taken these photographs of the street at different times of day.'

I look confused. He explains it's an artistic idea. My modern art education is lacking. At this stage, I don't think I really understood minimalist and modern art. And I looked at those grey photographs, those washed-out pictures with rising confusion.

He was a man who had flair, talent, who could pull anything off. Couldn't he see that these pictures were all the same. But he was doing something and that didn't matter. So I didn't say anything apart from encouraging comments. I wonder how good I am at being encouraging? I try. And I tried.

Yes, he was doing something and it was real, it was engaging with the environment, the real environment he was living in. It was positive.

His mouth moved slowly, it was clearly difficult for him to express himself. He was slow. His brain was moving slowly. I hated to see that. He was quick, fast, sharp. That's what I loved about him. Who was this man whose cogs turned so slowly, who found it hard to move his limbs, who seemed to be swimming in a sea of cotton wool. Now it was me who wanted to ask, who are you?

I tiptoed around the ward, trying not to disturb the patients, trying not to disturb the nurses, trying not to disturb the important duties of healing and curing being carried out in this important place.

I'd already had my absolutely torturous interview with the main consultant. She was cheery, straightforward and a strong woman. She asked me questions. I tried to answer them as honestly as I could, but somehow she made me feel terrible, made me feel shame, made me feel as though I had done dreadful things. But I felt terrible so quickly. Perhaps it was really me making myself feel shame about the whole business of this ill-advised marriage (I hadn't actually taken any advice at all).

Corporal punishment is a terrible thing. But I squirm quickly. And sometimes I think I'd prefer to be hit rather than be put on the spot and be made to ask questions that I didn't want to answer. It's as if someone is reaching their hands inside your stomach and is twisting it in knots. Shame, the emotion of shame, is a terrible, wounding, unbearable, filthy thing. It makes me feel dirty inside.

She accused me, but maybe it wasn't so much an accusation as a comment, an observation, of colluding with him to cover up his illness. That was exactly what I'd been doing, I realised when I thought about it later. Denial is colluding. And I'd been trying to manage him with the outside world to avoid offending people with his accusations. But I had never stopped him, so perhaps colluding was a bit strong. Or maybe it wasn't. But what I knew was that I was now tied up with his illness. I was a part of it. I had thought I was on the outside, but I was drifting, day by day by day, closer in, drawn into its hot fiery centre by psychological gravity.

Be careful who you orbit. Be careful to check the nature of the thing you love. Be careful to know the character of the person you love. If you're someone like me and you're by nature impulsive, if you're someone like me and you thrive on improvisation, be especially careful.

There's no one so blind as the person who doesn't want to see.

There's no one so vulnerable as those who love too hard, too fast, too well.

I've never loved anyone in the same ridiculous, abandoned way again. I've always loved with one eye open since. Once bitten twice shy. The very nature of love was changing for me, and while he was in that hospital it began to happen. I started to see who I was as well as who he was. They took away my rosy-tinted glasses and gave me new ones.

Next time I visited, the patients were together in the ward lounge watching television. I got on, naturally, with the nurses who specialised in mental health. They seemed like the people who were my friends. We naturally made friends. I enjoyed hearing their conversations. They were never dismissive or callous about health service users, unlike in general wards in my previous experience where I had heard some workers make fun of patients. But that, to be fair, was in another life, a long time ago, a life that seemed to be drifting even further away from who I was now.

Who am I?

An advert came on the television. Fields bursting into flames as a car drove through the burning crops. The song, the anthemic 'Take my breath away!' The room felt electric and some of the men were nearly standing out of their chairs. In-breaths here and there. A symphony of sharp intakes.

'This advert really excites some of them,' explained the nurse.

It really did, looking at the faces that had only a minute ago looked so calm.

I'll always remember that, how an advert can trigger such a strong reaction. Faces that are asleep, leaping into high alert. An advert having a phenomenal effect as if it was injecting adrenaline into the bloodstream.

There weren't many other visitors, looking back. I was the only woman I ever remember seeing on that ward. Of course, many of the other men were there for much longer than I had hoped that my husband would be there.

It was time for his meeting with the consultant. She was told I was there. She came to find me and beckoned me in for his meeting with her.

'I want you to see and hear for yourself how he is in the sessions,' she said. 'Come in.'

I went in. I'm not sure what I expected.

She sat behind the desk in a black and white dress. She was motherly. She reminded me of the kind but sensible doctor who had been the school doctor in Bolton. I sat on the side while she asked him questions. It was difficult to answer, I could see, but he looked her in the face, in the eyes, and answered. She asked questions about what things meant.

What did colours mean?

He told her that the colours black and white meant competence and safety.

She looked at her dress.

'Thank you very much,' she said.

I learned something of the alleyways and the avenues of his mind that day. I've forgotten the details, but I remember my sense of wonder and awe. What a mansion the mind is. What a landscape. Neurons and pathways popping, opening, starting and stopping. Gateways and rivers, cliffs on which you stand and look down as if you might fall off any second.

He was calm, he didn't argue, he was controlled. He didn't lose his temper, he didn't lose his cool. The consultant must have been pleased with his progress and soon they said he could come home. If I wanted.

If I wanted. Of course, I wanted. This was what I wanted. Him to be well enough to come home.

'Yes, of course.'

If he came home everything would be better now. It would all work out.

One of the mental nurses took me aside. Concerned, warm. Lovely eyes looking at me with warmth and concern.

'Are you sure,' he said, 'you want him to come home?'

'Of course.'

'Are you really sure? Are you not scared at all? How do you feel?'

'Of course, I want him to come home. Yes.'

The high dose medication was wearing off now. We'd see what happened next. Maybe this was just an episode set off by trauma. But the more episodes he had of psychosis, the more he'd have them repeatedly. The less chance there was of him being properly better.

Come home / don't come home / come home / don't come home.

Come home!

He came home.

The gingerly sensitiveness of those days. He'd been given the clean bill of health to come home from the hospital.

'Hello, welcome home, darling.'

He looked confused.

'Welcome home, I'll make you a cup of tea. I'll clean all the dishes. Everything is going to be great. Baby and I are so glad to have you home.'

What do you say to someone who has just come back from hospital like he has? What do you do? How do you make it okay? I'm not, I'm sorry, a very caring person. I'm not a very easy person. I'm an artist. I'm off in my own world. I'm a writer. I zonk out for ages. I'm a youngest child. I'm selfish and spoilt. I'm not a natural carer.

Hi, welcome home, I'll make tea. I'll clean up. I'll look after everything, keep it clean, sort out just everything.

Yeah, right.

His face so confused. His mouth chewing, chewing and slowly. Where had the man gone that I loved? Was he in there somewhere? He was covered in a mental blanket.

Could his eyes even see me? His pale blue eyes seemed to focus beyond me.

He wasn't terribly interested in the baby. He looked at her with disinterest. What was she to him? Did he even look at her with suspicion? Did he realise this was his daughter? Of course, he did, that was a silly thought. He knew exactly who we both were.

So summer is coming. Which is great. And I need some help looking after him, so let's go and see family.

We caught a plane to Belfast where his sister picked us up. We were going to Mullaghmore, a beautiful seaside village in Sligo, famous for being the place where Mountbatten was murdered by the IRA. Ben Bulben saw it from afar.

It's a most beautiful place. The grey churning water, the gothic castle rising out of the sea.

The locals really liked the Mountbattens, I heard. Terrible business. They don't come here anymore. Can you blame them? They asked and answered themselves. No. No one could. They understood.

The sky is amazingly dark and heavy. Then it lifts and everything is bright and light and wide. The clouds grow into mushrooms with large, fluffy tops.

The house came from an admiring client of his father. And everyone loved it. This place is a cool, wet, bright family home on a fine beach. Some of the boys are taking to water skiing. Water sports! It's still an Atlantic fishing port. We go to the pub and drink Guinness and eat salmon sandwiches. The sun comes in the evening as the beach faces West towards America. The sun is amazing light. It shines on everyone's faces.

Doesn't she look like S—? The girls say. It's S— all right.

The baby has blonde hair and blue eyes like both of us. She's pink and white and drinking the whole of Ireland up with her eyes.

We whisper to each other and chuckle. A black-and-white terrier runs in between our legs and sniffs our knees. Gurgles.

He takes little interest in anything. His eyes are vacant. It's the medication. I hope that as he takes less and less his energy will return and he'll be able to talk as fast as he used to talk and as well as he used to talk and as intelligently as I know he can. I can't wait for him to be on a lower medication. It feels wrong. I want to rip the paper off, the paper wrapped around his mind like packaging around a Christmas present, and shout.

See me! Look at me! Talk to me! I'm here.

This is all wrong, this is all wrong. Even here, in Paradise.

For I love Mullaghmore. It's an amazing place, where the Atlantic blows my mind. The seaweed may come to me at night and dazzles my senses with salt and lemon-freshness. I wake thinking I'm at the bottom of the ocean on a salt-bed, clutching at pearls.

It's time to go back to work. I've got some support from my mum and my dad, but my mum's still at work, teaching at Bolton Technical College. She's the best maths teacher. Her students would stop her as we went shopping in the centre of town, proud to see her. Miss, Miss! One of her students sought her out and insisted on moving in when I went to college. She was so persistent that my mother gave in. And my mother is very stubborn. Well, I got it from somewhere.

We're also workaholics and we believe in our work.

I went back to work. After all, he seemed fine, or finer or okay.

He'd never do anything to hurt the baby, would he? And he had the support of his sisters as now he'd acknowledged that he needed help and had gone to hospital. Everyone was pulling together, sailors on a ship in a storm, from the boy in the crow's nest to the captain in his clean white shirt and bright blue tails. We were all on the same page. Get him well. Get back on track.

But it wasn't easy. At all. I wasn't comfortable. What was going on when I was at work. I spent time on the phone that I shouldn't have spent.

The stress was terrible.

I worked at home as much as I could. The centre manager was really supportive. Sadly, I heard he died climbing a mountain in Sri Lanka. No one, not him, not anyone, knew how weak his heart was. Tragic.

One Tuesday bunking off, playing table tennis with S—, the Asian Arts Development Officer on the Isle of Dogs discovered that I wouldn't hit the ping pong ball on a backhand without spinning it. I wasn't playing the game of life well either. All my strokes were going off wildly to the left and the right. They wouldn't land square on the table.
S— was always hilarious and I don't know what he said but I spent most of the time curled up, laughing so much I got a stitch.

Bunches of flowers arrived at work for S—. He was being courted by more than one eager woman. The card said: 'to a Secret Asian'. Secret Asians was the name of the comedy group he was doing with N— S—, the start of the show that would become Goodness Gracious Me. No one would send me flowers anymore, I thought sadly.

Once I had seen a dead dog, desiccated on a road in Spain. Sad. So dead it was dry. Dry like a rib cage. I had taken a black-and-white photograph to fix its contrast in the hot sun. Nothing could be as dead as that dog. Apart from this romance. I'd have to use my imagination in future. It would have to happen in my mind as it could no longer be part of my real life. I'd sit in an armchair, watching period dramas on Sunday evening television. Or read large print Mills and Boon stories from the library, bottle glasses on, stockings slipping into wrinkles down around my ankles.

Life had given me my own bunch of skeleton flowers, brittle, white, flowers that would haunt me. Dead violets. Grey lilac. Bleached and soulless tulips.

WHO ARE YOU?

Falling in love – and then finding out too late who the other person is– is normal. But when you have visions, like he did, when you hear voices, that person is changed. He no longer knew who I was. The voices must be whispering, must be talking to him.

She's not who she says she is. She's a liar. She's working for them. They're all out to get you. You can trust no one.

The voices talk to him every day. The medicine blocks them out, but they're still there. As he takes less medication, as he stops taking the medication whether he forgets, whether it's casual, whether it's on purpose, whatever the voices tell him, for whatever reason, those voices come back.

I know he's not getting better.

I use my super-powers of denial, but they're no longer any good. And I'm running out of strength.

I cope by becoming a mouse. I become a grey mouse. I creep around the house, hiding, trying not to set him off. I don't want him to be angry. I only want peace.

Family therapy, perhaps that would help?
We had scheduled sessions following on from hospital care.
We went to our meeting.
We had to do this, it was recommended. It was our hope.
That little hour-long meeting, that was our hope.

It was difficult to get the extra childcare I needed for the session, but it was arranged, and in we went.

A small, bearded social worker sat with the two of us and we chatted.

I tried to be as amenable as I come. I went into my usual people-pleaser mode, trying to make everything okay. I'm happy admitting to guilt. I'm even comfortable admitting to guilt. Maybe it's a religious-influenced condition from my mother's Methodism. Work hard. Don't drink. Work harder.

I went, I talked.

He came with me.

He didn't talk.

The first one went badly but maybe the next one would be better.

He refused to go again.

Come on your own, said the social worker. This is for you. Make an effort for you.

But what was the point? I knew everything was messed up. And it was so much effort and cost to get a childminder. I couldn't see how it would help me at all. It was no practical help. What I needed was something else entirely. It would just drain me of time, money and energy. And I seemed to be supplying all the answers during the session.

It was like visiting a nosy uncle who just wanted the gossip. Who wouldn't give any opinions, advice or useful suggestions. He was small, had a ginger beard and looked like a garden gnome. That was cruel. But I couldn't get that vision out of my head.

I saw him sitting on a rock with a fishing rod. At the weekends. He came to life when the alarm went in the morning. On Saturdays he turned back into plaster.

Of course, if S— had agreed to carry on the sessions it would've been different.

What was there in it for me if I went on my own?

PEACE. That's the precious gift that we give each other. A bit of beautiful peace where we can be happy and content. PEACE in our time. PEACE for a moment. I want peace.

I no longer want excitement, fun, crazy times. PEACE would be enough for me.

I could grow fat on peace. Like a cow grazing on green grass.

I could suntan myself on a peaceful beach, turn my skin a pleasant brown. I could lie on the beach of peace. A holiday.

I needed a holiday from my marriage. But every time I took a holiday, or a trip to escape from the stress, I returned and the stress was still there.

Go home.

I talked to my friends and asked for their advice.

Go home.

Go back to your home.

But I loved London. My arts community friends. I felt I had achieved something in my life by settling here. It's not easy you know.

GO HOME!

I bloody wouldn't!

Night-time. Sleep time. Time of peace.

The baby was so good. She did everything right. She was already sleeping through the night.

WHO ARE YOU?

You know who I am.

WHO ARE YOU?

He locked me outside of the house.

I panicked. I couldn't get in. What about my baby. She was still inside.

Now I had to beg – please let me in.

He let me back in.

Now the countdown had begun. Even my powers of denial couldn't help me any longer. They had run out of steam. I was counting down inside. I wouldn't go home. Where could I go? What could I do? Surely he should leave and we should stay in the house. Could that happen?

You'd think it would be possible. From the outside, it would seem the law could help you with that, but that's not how it was for me, for many others. The first rule is to protect yourself and your children. That can't be done by hanging around with someone out of control and unpredictable. By staying with someone you can't trust.

I was dreaming less if anything, at this time, as I was no longer deep sleeping. I was always on the alert. Or if I did sleep, I woke up with a start and forget whatever I was dreaming. There was no longer any luxury, no time to remember dreams, to turn them over in my head.

Dreaming was for those with time and peace. I had neither.

What was going to happen next?

I knew that the world was going to tilt over and that everything would be different on the other side.

I went to the doctor's to talk about it and see what they could do. Could they help him?

No, they couldn't talk about his case with me. It was a breach of confidentiality, said the GP. But you look stressed. So he gave me a sick note. Thank goodness. I enjoyed work, I was less stressed at work, if anything, but with a sick note I could stay home and look after the baby, rather than the alternatives – send her to my mother's or the childminder, trust my husband not to neglect her. A sick note was the best thing.

It was a year since she'd been born. It was the dead of winter one more time. The year's midnight. I was in the dark.

My life had been leading towards the light. Each day getting brighter, more vivid. I was growing in strength and insight. Then I met S— and the world blazed so brightly I could hardly see it. It became colourful, confused almost, psychedelic, multi-coloured. Then it began to fade, day by day. Now there was hardly a glimmer to light my days by.

Let alone the nights.

It was cold. The cold of snow. The cold of wonderful, calming, quietening snow. It was coming.

There's a moment before snow comes when it warms. When the freezing cold lifts its bite for a second and you can feel it's coming, it's coming!

The snow is so magical when it falls. Disney know this. The tinkle that says, Christmas is coming folks, wrap up warm. Get those snug knits on, red jumpers, knitted scarves. Sleigh bells-a-jingling in the night-blue stars popping in to see what's up, down below on these frosted-cake cities of yours.

Snow falls on the roofs and it makes them white, so birds can walk across and leave their fork footprints. Snow cures us all with its fringe of purity. Who can feel bad in the snow? It's the promise of a new beginning for everyone.

Time to sing carols, especially those wavery descants – high as a songbird, at the top of the tree. Can't catch me, I'm the highest, the purest, the clearest of all. Up above the world so high... with the stars.

I start to sing and hum. Insanely I feel happy, pure, lifted and clear through.

I've heard people feel like this before suicide. That a kind of ecstasy takes over some people when they know it's in their power to do what they will, even if that control means the worst thing of all. But to feel in control of yourself, after months, years of feeling powerless, is incredible. It's beautiful. It's out of this world.

It's on the coldest of cold nights when I know –snap, like a frost– that this is it. This is the end of the road. It was a beautiful ecstasy, a freedom. But it was born of terror. Let me tell you how it happened.

We were sitting together in the kitchen. This was the area of our conversations. That round table didn't necessarily breed harmony. The hard, white round table, that moon table, was not somewhere of equality, but somewhere to bite.

That evening we began to bite each other. I bit him as well.

Not literally, there was no literal biting, but we were mental sharks chasing each other. My frustration had blown the fuse and I was devil-may-care, whatever-may-come, do-whatever-you-will-I-just-don't care-any-more. So we fought.

Not for long, because he won.

He pushed me against the wall and began to squeeze my throat.

This was it. The end. I won't be here after this. All that promise gone.

And my brain knew it was time to say goodbye to my lovely parents, to my lovely life, my lovely baby. Staying in London had got me killed. My stubbornness had got me killed. My love had got me killed.

Then the pressure relieved and I gasped.

As I came to, I knew it was all over. Not for me, but for this marriage, this love affair. It was totally and absolutely killed, stone-dead.

I was grateful in a way. I knew I was so stubborn that I wouldn't admit failure even when it was staring me in the face.

Some force of nature had saved me because my clever mind hadn't done it.

A phone call to the police, who came quickly. They waited, happily, talking kindly to him while I got a couple of black plastic bin-bags and threw a few of my worldly possessions inside. Mostly it was baby clothes ha ha. And a few clothes for myself. Come with me, my baby, it's time to go.

Maybe I'd get a few things back later when my brother-in-law came by to pick some stuff up for me, or my dad. I didn't know though.

I'm sentimental about things... some things... I sniffed as I mentally said bye-bye to my black-and-white Stratocaster that my mum had bought me. I never did learn to play it.

A friend of mine who lived not too far had agreed that my baby and I could stay with him. He was very kind. A fellow musician. I've noticed that musicians are often kind to each other, are often good friends. You work together. You get used to being together. There's an intimacy there that's worth fortunes.

My lovely baby ... my creation. Our creation. In my arms. Because of police insurance, we couldn't travel in the Panda car, so they drove next to me as I walked on foot, boots careful not to slip on the hard pavement. It wasn't far to my friend's flat.

Fortunately, the flat was very secure, so I knew I'd be safe there. Built for modern residents who wanted gated communities, it had intercom and buzzers. I was grateful for that modern obsession with security right now. Although it had been built for rich clients it couldn't be sold to them after the market crash, so now it was being rented out by a housing association.

I stood outside in my favourite coat. Blue-green-grey, with a wool grey lining. So stylish. I'd bought it from Brown's down-town and it had cost me 300 pounds. I loved it. I would've never bought such an expensive coat if S— hadn't encouraged me. I didn't think I was worth it. Or perhaps I just didn't think you should spend so much money on clothes. I probably never could or would again. I stood inside it, hugged by its friendly expensive softness, hugging my baby on the corner of the street.

I still loved my coat, but it embarrassed me.

It was a symbol of how I had bitten off more than I could chew. Overreached myself.

194

Above me the flakes of winter were falling. They landed on my hair, they landed on my shoulders, they landed on my sleeves.

At my side there were two black bin liners stuffed with clothes and baby things.

Whenever I'm stressed, or imagining a scene, or dreaming, or at any time, music comes to me. I don't ask for it. It just arrives in my ears, in my brain, thrumming and humming and vibrating through my bones.

Sometimes it's music I don't recognise, like an Ennio Morricone symphony for a film that's never been made, glorious, rich and atmospheric. And sometimes it's a little nursery tune from my childhood – twinkle, twinkle little star, how impossibly far you are... classics get a little twist in my pot of memory.

For no reason at all, I looked up towards the stars and, inside, began to sing.

'Hark! The herald angels sing.'

EPILOGUE

A few days later, having settled in at my friend's and having let my family know and with my support system from them in place, I went back to the house. I went back to see my husband. Why? To be honest, I was worried about him.

I looked outside and saw him inside, in the dark, sitting in the dark. No lights.

What might happen? He could kill himself. Yes, that's what they'd been most worried about in the Rachel Ward. That was the most likely danger with people who had psychosis, I was told. That they'd kill themselves. You had to be careful.

I'd feel terrible if I let that happen for want of a little intervention, a phone call. I went and reported it to the doctor.

She came, how kind, that evening. In coat and scarf, there that evening in the cold. She knocked on the door and spoke to him for a little while. How was he? Was he doing okay? Did he need anything, was there anything that the doctor could do? His wife had called her because she was worried. I stood in the background smiling and nodding and looking uncomfortably foolish and embarrassed as he wouldn't talk to me.
He was angry. I can't remember exactly what he said but it was

unpleasant. I can remember the tone which rings around my head like a grater, a metal ball, an evil resonance.

The doctor and I left, and he shut the door. It was just me and her beneath the street-light. On that memorable stretch of road, the ring road around the Isle of Dogs, next to the orange flashing Belisha beacons.

'He seems to be particularly hostile towards you,' she said.

That was a warning.

I had to accept that warning.

His health was no longer my business.

I couldn't do anything, she was telling me to keep away.

The doctor was warning me to stay away, to look after myself, to look after my baby and not to be foolish and foolhardy, to give up my impossible mission of love.

Love isn't a magical cure, it can't do everything.

Here ends the book about love in the Isle of Dogs. Since then even more, high, tall, shiny buildings have joined the cluster at Canary Wharf. Finance has picked up, collapsed and picked up again. It rises and falls in waves. New structures go up, people keep making their millions and losing them. And on that U-shaped ring-road, towards the Greenwich foot tunnel, our house is still there. Others live there now. Perhaps there have been multiple owners, many different families. I hope they're happy in this beautiful home that he built.

We're very happy, my grown-up baby and I. Thank goodness.

But how fragile is the line between happiness and unhappiness.

I'm so grateful to be on this side of the glass.

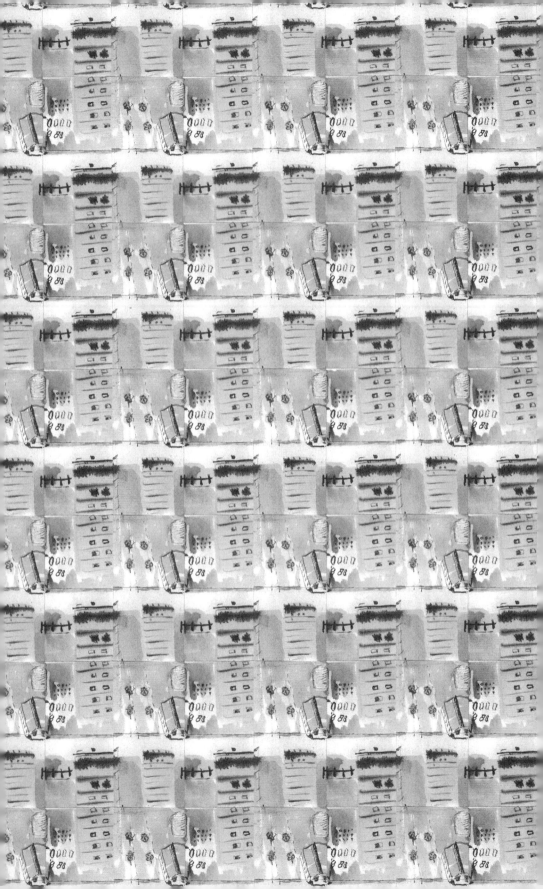

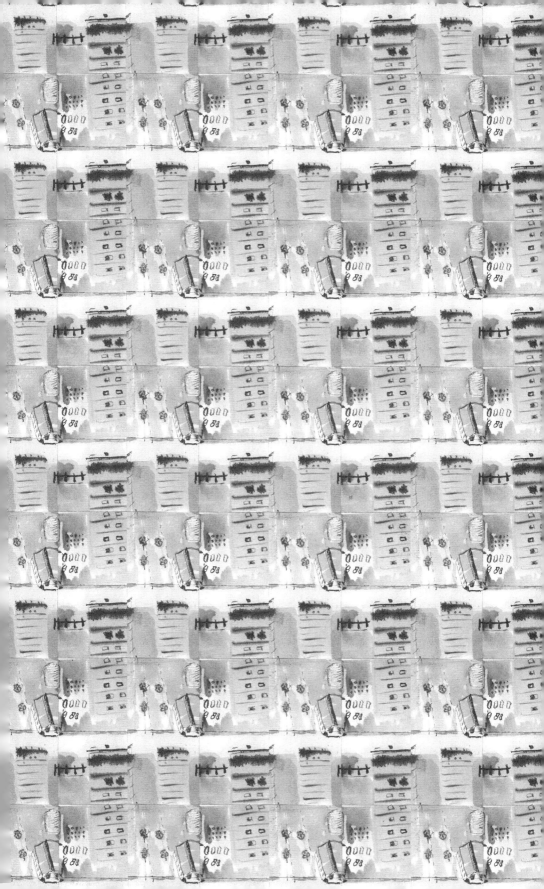